THE
ILLUSTRATED ENCYCLOPAEDIA
OF ANIMAL LIFE

THE ANIMAL KINGDOM

The strange and wonderful ways of
mammals, birds, reptiles, fishes and
insects. A new and authentic natural
history of the wild life of the world

VOLUME 16

FREDERICK DRIMMER, M.A.
EDITOR-IN-CHIEF

GEORGE G. GOODWIN
*Associate Curator of Mammals,
The American Museum of Natural
History*

CHARLES M. BOGERT
*Curator of Amphibians and Reptiles,
The American Museum of Natural
History*

**DEAN AMADON
E. THOMAS GILLIARD**
*Associate Curators of Birds,
The American Museum of Natural History*

CHRISTOPHER W. COATES *Curator*
JAMES W. ATZ *Assistant Curator*
*Aquarium of The New York Zoological
Society*

JOHN C. PALLISTER
Research Associate, Insects, The American Museum of Natural History

ODHAMS BOOKS LIMITED, LONG ACRE, LONDON

Colour photographs supplied by members of The Free Lance Photographers Guild except as otherwise individually credited.

THE SYNTOMIDS—OFTEN MISTAKEN FOR WASPS

The family Syntomidae, also sometimes called Amatidae, is a small one, reaching its greatest development in the hotter countries. A few species extend northward into the eastern United States. The syntomids are small, brightly coloured, day-flying moths, found around field flowers. They are frequently mistaken for wasps or other hymenopterous insects, because their bright colours usually show a great deal of contrast, including such combinations as black, red, and yellow.

TIGER MOTHS AND WOOLLY BEARS

To the layman, the caterpillars of the tiger moth are perhaps more often noticed than the adults, for these caterpillars are the familiar Woolly Bears. In the autumn, many of them leave their eating places and start out in search of a new home, some looking for a place to hibernate, and some for a nice place to spin a rough cocoon. As they spin, the hairs on the body are mixed with the silk.

These creatures are also called "hedgehog caterpillars", for, when disturbed, they curl into a compact mass, presenting to the disturber an armour of hairs. The adults are quite variable, but they are mostly thick-bodied and hairy. They are white, brown, red, yellow, or combinations of these colours, frequently with black dots or lines added. In this family (Arctiidae), there are about 2,500 known species. They range from the colder regions to the hottest.

The Salt-marsh Caterpillar, *Estigmene acraea,* is common throughout North America. Its popular name was applied many years ago when numbers of them were seen in salt marshes. However, they feed on a great variety of plants and are regarded as a serious pest by vegetable growers.

Nevertheless, one is tempted to forgive these caterpillars for the damage they do, because of the beautiful moths that they are going to become. The male is all white. The female's rear wings are yellow, spotted with small black dots, and she has a reddish abdomen.

The Virginia Tiger Moth, *Diacrisia virginica,* has white wings, flecked with a few faint, black specks, and a yellowish abdomen. This moth may be seen resting in a garden, for its caterpillar loves to feed on many garden plants. *Diacrisia vulpinaria* is the European representative and is rather similar in appearance.

The Isabella Tiger Moth, *Isia isabella*, has all-yellow wings, flecked with a few tiny brown spots, and a reddish abdomen. This is the woolliest of all woolly bears, the one that may be seen in the autumn hurrying across a road.

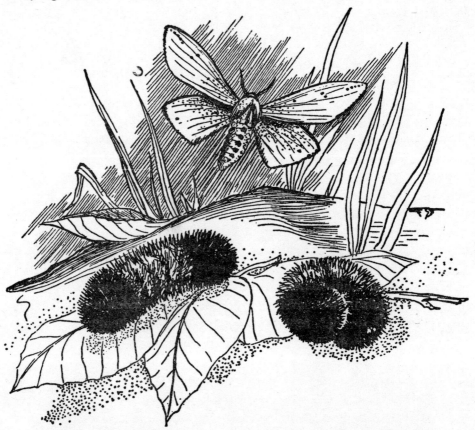

THE RAMBLING WOOLLY BEAR GROWS INTO AN EXQUISITE TIGER MOTH

Have you ever tried the woolly bear as a forecaster of the winter's weather? If the rust-coloured band around this caterpillar's middle is broad, it is supposed to be a sign that the winter will not be cold. A walk along any path in the autumn may show you woolly bears mostly with wide bands—but a walk the next day along another path a mile away may show you woolly bears mostly with narrow bands! The woolly bear spends the winter under leaves and debris. In the spring it spins a cocoon from which it will emerge as a lovely little orange-coloured moth.

This woolly bear is not engaging in a contest with the traffic, but is hurrying to find a snug place in which to curl up and pass the winter. If everything has gone well with it, it comes forth on sunny days, eats a little more of its favourite food, plantain, and finally spins its cocoon under a loose stone, a log, or bark.

As almost everyone knows, the woolly bear is black at both ends and reddish brown in the middle. In some years this bright centre will be unusually broad, and then we can remember a bit of old weather lore: that the more brown on the woolly bear, the milder we can expect the winter to be.

Any resemblance between this insect and future temperatures is purely coincidental.

The Autumn Webworm, *Hyphantria cunea,* is a greyish-white moth, flecked with brown spots. These spots may be plentiful or almost lacking. The caterpillars are equally variable, and live in a colony-nest of loosely spun silk entirely covering the branches of a tree. It is often confused with the Spring Webworm, *Malacosoma americana.*

FORESTER MOTHS

This family (Agaristidae) is mentioned here only because of one important species, the Eight-spotted Forester, *Alypia octomaculata.* Other *Alypias* are also called foresters and occupy other regions, but the eight-spot occurs in the north-eastern United States. It is a small, velvety-black moth, one and one-half inches in wing-spread, with eight yellow and white spots, two to each wing, the largest at the base of the rear wings. They are seen near grapevines because the caterpillars feed on these and on the Virginia creeper, and are frequently very destructive.

NOCTUIDS, OR OWLET MOTHS—
THEIR EYES HAVE AN ORANGE GLOW

The name noctuid comes from the Latin word *noctua,* meaning "night owl", and a more appropriate name for these moths could hardly have been found. They fly at night, and their eyes shine with a beautiful orange glow stimulated by any reflected light. They are largely phototropic (meaning that, like certain plants, they turn toward light) and they can usually be found around lights.

WHEN AND HOW TO COLLECT THEM

Another and more exciting way of collecting them is by "sugaring". A mixture of brown sugar or molasses, with enough water to make a thick syrup, added to a little stale beer or rum, to soothe the insects that gather for the feast, is spread with a large brush on tree trunks or fence posts at dusk. The trees selected should be along a convenient, open pathway or trail, or margin of woods, rather than in the deep forest, although a few trees in thick woods may be tried experimentally. A lone tree in a field often attracts many moths. A circuitous trail of half a mile or a mile makes a fine route.

Warm, muggy summer or autumn nights usually yield best results. After dark with flashlight and net, start your rounds. Approach each bait tree quietly with flash unlit. Hold the net under the spot baited, and then turn on the flashlight. If conditions are right, you may be amazed at the things gathered for the banquet. There will be moths, mostly noctuids, beetles, grasshoppers, crickets, millipedes and centipedes, and ants.

If ants collect, they tend to drive away other creatures with their scurrying around, and will even attack them.

The reaction of the insects to the light is also interesting. At your first approach, on the flash of the light some will drop, perhaps into the net as intended. Others may fly upward. If you are quick enough you may catch some of these on the wing. Others will sit calmly, allowing you to place a wide-mouthed killing jar over them. Hold it there a moment until the insect flutters back into the jar. At first you will attempt to secure everything in sight; but after a few experiences your eye will quickly select what is rare from among the throng. At any rate, the author hopes you will have many enjoyable evenings, as he has had, taking them.

The Noctuidae family is one of the largest. More than twenty thousand species have been described, at least 2,500 of them living in North America. They are largely small moths with wing-spreads of two inches or under, mottled brown or grey in colour. However, a few are brightly coloured, and some reach a considerable size.

FACTS ABOUT NOCTUID CATERPILLARS

The caterpillars are sometimes called Army Worms and Cutworms. Many of them do considerable damage, and gardeners "cuss" all caterpillars for this reason. You may be assured, however, that not all noctuid caterpillars are injurious; in fact, many are quite beneficial because they control vegetation that might become too possessive of the ground.

HOW TO DESTROY THEM

Cutworms may be destroyed by placing a poison bran mixture in various spots in the garden in the spring before plants are set out or seed is sown. The mixture is prepared by mixing one part, by weight, of Paris green, to twenty-five parts of bran and sufficient molasses thinned with water to make a thick mash. Chickens, as well as dogs, cats, and other pets, like this poisonous mixture, so precautions should be taken to prevent them from getting at it. You can do this by placing the mash under heavy, or weighted, boxes or pails that cannot be overturned. A few handfuls of mash should take care of the average garden.

In this book we have space to mention only a few of the noctuids. If you wish to study the family more intensively, there are many specialized reports and papers on the group. If you should become deeply interested in the noctuids, you could spend a lifetime studying the North American species alone, without ever attempting to become acquainted with the exotic ones about which little is known.

TUSSOCK MOTHS

The Liparidae, also called Lymantriidae, is a small family, but important and well known for its destructive species. The moths are small and not particularly outstanding in appearance. The caterpillars frequently occur in such numbers as to completely strip the leaves from the trees where they cluster.

The White-marked Tussock Moth, *Hemerocampa leucostigma*, is perhaps the best known of this family, for it is widespread over the entire eastern part of North America. In the West it is replaced by the California species, *vetusta*. It is the caterpillar from which the moth gets its name, and a most exquisite creature it is, with its four white tussocks of hairs, its red head, and pencils of long, black hair standing erect, two from the thorax, and one on the last segment, not to mention the yellow and black stripes on the body.

When grown, it spins a rough cocoon of silk interlaced with the hairs from its body, placing it usually in a crevice on the trunk of a tree, or in any other sheltered place. Under the eaves, or the edges of the clapboards of a house is a favourite spot. Sometimes four or five cocoons are massed together.

INSECT PARASITISM

It is estimated that only ten per cent of the caterpillars live to reach maturity. In addition to the predatory birds that destroy countless numbers, the caterpillars are beset by parasites. Over twenty hymenopterous and dipterous parasites on these caterpillars have been discovered, these parasites being attacked by hyperparasites, and these in turn by parasites. This pageant of animal existence is one of the most interesting cases of insect parasitism.

Very few people are familiar with the mature male moth, for it is a small, drab insect. The female is wingless, a fat little ash-grey creature who crawls out of her cocoon house and sits on the doorstep awaiting her lover. She then deposits her four hundred, or more, eggs on the top of the cocoon, covers them with a frothy secretion, which hardens into a waterproof covering, and dies. There may be as many as three generations a year. The winter is passed in the egg stage.

The Gypsy Moth, *Porthetria dispar*, was introduced from Europe into the United States in 1868 by an amateur entomologist experimenting with some material. It was to prove a very costly and disastrous experiment.

Some of the moths escaped from captivity, and in no time a colony was established in Massachusetts. Rapidly spreading, the gypsy moth had caused immense destruction before control measures were started. These controls have been successful in confining it to the New England states, but there is no telling when it may accidentally become established in another area. If it is discovered in a new area, this fact should be immediately reported to the insect authorities.

The moths appear in July but may be seen for several months. The male is brown, with a wing-spread of less than two inches. The female is larger and whitish. It seldom flies, a fact which has been an important factor in preventing the spread of the insect.

The eggs are laid in masses ranging in number from several hundred to nearly a thousand. The mass is covered with scales from the body of the adult and appears as a rounded, whitish object. Egg masses can usually be found on the under-side of foliage, tree limbs, and stones, as well as on wagons and cars, and wherever the female can crawl after emerging from its pupa. The caterpillars feed at night and congregate during the day in masses on the limbs of trees or other protected spots. They are known to feed on over five hundred species of plants, including the cone-bearing trees.

The Brown-tail Moth, *Euproctis chrysorrhoea*, was also introduced to America from Europe. How it arrived no one knows, but it is now firmly established from Connecticut and Rhode Island northward to Nova Scotia.

The female brown-tail flies readily, and new colonies may easily become established from a wind-blown insect. Fortunately, the prevailing winds are from the west so that drifting insects would be blown out to sea rather than inland. The moths are whitish and can be distinguished by the brown hairs on the end of the abdomen. These are less conspicuous in the male. These moths appear in July and are attracted to lights more frequently than the gypsy moth.

The egg mass, usually on the under-side of a leaf, is covered with the brown scales from the moth's abdomen. Hatching in a couple of weeks, the tiny caterpillars live in a colony on the tender terminal foliage, which they cover with a webbing of silk. It is in this same nest that the half-grown caterpillars pass the winter. In the spring they resume their feeding, pupating in late spring.

The larvae are covered with brownish hairs, with a row of white tufts along each side. The hairs, particularly the brown ones, are barbed and poisonous. One need not come into direct contact with the insects to be attacked by them, for the hairs are carried by the wind, causing intense irritation to the skin, where they lodge. Some individuals are more allergic than others to these hairs.

TENT CATERPILLARS

A medium-large family (Lasiocampidae) found throughout the world, the tent caterpillars are poorly represented in North America by a few small species. What the family lacks in species it makes up in numbers. Some of the most destructive of all species are found in America.

Asia, Africa, and South America have some larger moths of this family. A few of the tropical species are valuable for the silk they produce, for the family is closely related to the true silkworms.

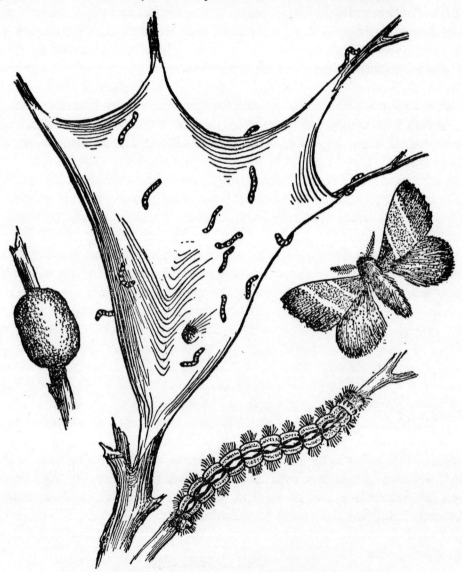

TENT CATERPILLARS LIKE TO CAMP ON WILD CHERRY TREES

Tent caterpillars lead an interesting communal life, generally on a wild cherry tree, but when they cannot find one they may disfigure cultivated trees with their curious webs (*centre*). The grown caterpillars leave their tents to find a place to weave a papery cocoon and, as there are a great many of them in each tent, they can create quite a bit of activity for yards around an infested tree. The moth is yellowish or reddish brown. Pictured at the left, encircling a twig, is the egg mass—it contains three hundred eggs or more.

The Tent Caterpillar, *Malacosoma americana*, is familiar to everyone in the east of the United States, because of its destructive larvae and the unsightly nests they spin in the trees, usually in the fork of a tree.

To the caterpillars, the nest is a wonderful structure. They sally out from it at night to feed, returning to the nest during the day or in stormy weather for protection.

Each caterpillar, as it travels along a branch, spins a thread of silk; others follow, until trails of silk radiate from the nest to the feeding stations. These trails then provide convenient return routes.

When fully grown, the caterpillar gets the wanderlust and, either crawling or dropping to the ground, starts hunting for a place in which to pupate. When it has found a suitable crevice or protected spot it builds a paper-like white cocoon and fastens it in a mesh of scattered threads.

The small, inconspicuous brown moths emerge in July. They can be recognized by the two fine, white lines which cross the front wings. They soon lay their eggs in masses which completely encircle a slender twig on one of their favourite food trees. They are partial to apple, pear, and wild cherry.

The Forest Tent Caterpillar, *Malacosoma disstria*, is sociable, but constructs no compact nest like that of the *americana*. It feeds on a variety of leaf-shedding forest trees and ranges over a large part of North America. The Great Basin Tent Caterpillar, *fragilis*, replaces the eastern species in the West. The Lackey Moth, *nuestrium*, is the European tent caterpillar and is also very destructive.

The Syrian Silkworm, *Pachypasa otus*, was a valuable silk-producing insect. The silk was used by the Greeks and Romans long before the introduction, about A.D. 550, of the Chinese silkworm. Its silk, which is a beautiful white, competed with that produced by Chinese silkworms until the late 1800's. *Borocera madagascariensis*, known as the Bibindandy, produces a beautiful silk. As its scientific name indicates, it is a native of Madagascar.

SILKWORMS—SPINNERS OF THE ORIENT

Less than a hundred species make up the silkworm family (Bombycidae), and they are all confined to eastern Asia.

The Chinese Silkworm, *Bombyx mori*, is the outstanding example in this group. It has so long been associated with man that it is almost domesticated and probably could not live by itself outdoors. Individuals have been liberated in what were thought to be favourable areas, but always failed to survive. Through the ages, many silkworm races have been developed to fit certain requirements, such as climate, productiveness, and the quality of the silk.

The adults are creamy white, heavy abdomened, and have a wing expanse of less than two inches. They never fly. About three hundred eggs are laid in a scattered fashion around the female. Commercial growers feed the larvae on mulberry leaves spread out in a thin layer on trays which slide into supporting frames. The larvae do not roam but feed contentedly on the leaves. A new supply of leaves is provided each day. In addition to the white and black mulberry normally used, they will also feed on osage orange and lettuce. In some instances, there may be as many as six broods a year.

The larvae feed for about forty-five days and spin their cocoons, from which the adults emerge in about two weeks. The cocoons to be used for commercial purposes are soaked in hot water, a procedure which kills the pupa but allows the silk to be unwound and reeled with ease.

GEOMETERS, OR MEASURING WORMS

A very large family (Geometridae) of smallish (though sometimes large in the tropics), more or less fragile moths, the geometers are usually seen resting on tree trunks or fences with their wings spread out flat. They depend upon the maze of zig-zag lines or other baffling designs on their wings to prevent detection.

The caterpillars have no legs in the middle of the body, as do most other larvae. They therefore travel in a series of loops, by stretching out and taking firm hold with the three pairs of true legs on the thorax. The body is then looped, with the rear end brought forward to take hold with its two pairs of legs. It is this looping of the caterpillars that has given them such names as measuring worms, inch worms, span-worms, spanners, and loopers. The scientific name means "earth measurers", and it fits them well, for they seem to be forever on the move. As the old saying informs us, no summer picnic is complete without a few measuring worms taking your measurement for a new suit of clothes.

Although the family is very large (a thousand species have been described in North America alone), the colouring of many is so similar that we will consider only two of the more common species.

The Autumn Cankerworm, *Alsophila pometaria*, is a conspicuous moth in wooded areas in the autumn, not through its beauty but because of the numbers that flutter about. The male is small and tan, with darker lines and markings. The female is a stay-at-home and a drab little creature. She is wingless, and for her view of the world she is content to crawl slowly on a tree trunk.

This little lady makes up for her lack of beauty by the batch of exquisite eggs she lays in November. The late Dr. Frank E. Lutz, the well-known entomologist, likened the appearance of the individual egg to a tiny "grey flower pot having a grey cover decorated with a dark central spot and a dark ring near the edge". The batch of eggs is placed carefully in close, regular rows and must be studied with the aid of a lens.

In the spring, from each of these "flower pots", instead of a lovely flower a voracious caterpillar pushes up the lid and crawls out to spend the spring feasting on the leaves of a great number of trees.

When the hot days of July come, the caterpillar drops to the ground on a silken thread and burrows into the cool soil, spins a rough cocoon, pupates, and does not emerge until late autumn. A few do not emerge until spring, when they may be seen flying with the Spring Cankerworms, to the confusion of the amateur collector.

The Spring Cankerworm Moth, *Paleacrita vernata*, is a small, pale-tan moth that flies in the early spring, shortly after the snow is off the ground. As in the case of the autumn cankerworm, the female is wingless. In most localities, the spring cankerworm is much more common. Its caterpillar is responsible for great damage, for it strips the leaves from many trees. It was largely because of this species, together with some other geometrid larvae, that the English sparrow was introduced into the United States, to feed upon the insect. The American caterpillars did not appeal to the birds, which turned out to be destructive in other ways themselves.

BAGWORMS—MOTHS WITH UNUSUAL HABITS

This family (Psychidae) of medium-sized moths is interesting, not so much for colour or shape, as for its unusual habits. As soon as its caterpillars are hatched, they proceed to build about themselves little homes of silk, into which are woven bits of twigs, leaves, bark, or other debris. From this habit come their common names—bagworms, bag moths, case moths, and basketworms. Each species makes its characteristic type of case. In most species the case of the female moth differs from that of the male moth.

The females, as far as is known, are wingless, and spend their entire lives in the cases they started for themselves as very young caterpillars. The males have dark bodies, and for a short time after emerging from their pupae they have dark wings. Their wing scales, however, are so loosely attached that they are soon lost, leaving the moth with transparent wings. It is in this condition that one usually sees them.

The species are not numerous in the temperate region. Tropical and subtropical countries have several hundred, some of which construct bags several inches in length. Australians complain about bagworms, each with a case as large as an ordinary cigar, hanging side by side on trees from which they have eaten the leaves.

The Common Bagworm of eastern North America is not nearly as long as its technical name, *Thyridopteryx ephemeraeformis*. The adult male has long, feathery antennae; a black, slender, tapering body; and smoky, transparent wings that were dull black when it first emerged. The adult female has no wings, no legs, no eyes, no antennae. She is just a soft, yellowish-white, maggot-like creature. She deposits her numerous white eggs in the case where she lives, and then dies, her body plugging the case up against intruders.

The caterpillars do not hatch out until the following spring. Then they weave their little cases and fasten them to the twigs of almost any kind of tree or shrub, although they prefer evergreens. Their bags can be seen everywhere and at any time, hanging even on the trees along city streets and on other isolated trees and shrubs. Where there are enough of them they can strip the leaves from a tree, but this does not happen often.

SLUG CATERPILLARS—SOME HAVE DANGEROUS SPINES

Its curious sluglike caterpillars are the most remarkable thing about the family Limacodidae. With practically no feet, they slide around on the surface of the leaf. Beware of them if they belong to a species with spines, for the spines are easily broken off and can become embedded in your flesh, causing extreme irritation. The author is inclined to believe they are not poisonous, although many books claim they are.

People vary widely in their reactions to the spines. Not only is the caterpillar to be avoided, but the thin cocoon it spins has the spines interwoven in the silk, making it a dangerous object to handle care-lessly. Fortunately, not many of the species are so armed. The family has had a number of scientific names, including Cochlidiidae, Eucleidae, and Heterogeneidae.

SOME WEIRD CATERPILLARS AND THEIR TINY MOTHS

The strange caterpillar on the left is well named the "saddleback"; the saddle is brown, on a pale green "saddle pad"; the rest of the body is reddish brown. Note the hairs or spines on the saddleback—they sting like nettles. Above this larva is its small moth, which is light-and-dark reddish brown. The creature at the lower right is also a caterpillar—it is called the "hag moth", or "monkey slug caterpillar", and you have to see one to believe it. Both of these caterpillars can be found on fruit trees.

The Saddleback Moth, *Sibine stimulea*, is a common species in the eastern United States, and its caterpillar is one greatly to be feared. Don't, however, let this prevent you—if you are in this area—from attempting to find one of these creatures to look at from a safe distance. About one inch long, it is green, with each end brown, and with a brown saddle mark in the centre of its back. Pointing outward from each end are two prominent, spine-covered, fleshy protuberances. Along each side are a number of tufts of yellow spines which can sting far worse than nettles.

Every summer, some of these attractive caterpillars are brought or sent into the author's office, carefully housed in an old pickle bottle. The universal question is: "What can it be? I've never seen anything like it."

This caterpillar feeds on a variety of vegetation. Look for it on cherry, apple, or pear trees, or on corn. When fully grown, the caterpillar wanders some distance, seeking a place to spin its cocoon. The author knows of one case where a saddleback caterpillar wandered into a bureau drawer and, deciding the soft underclothing was a good place to pupate, carefully spun its cocoon. Not noticing the cocoon, the owner of the apartment, a woman, donned the garment from the drawer and soon suffered a severe case of skin irritation which sent her to hospital for some time. The adult moth is small and of a rich brown colour.

The Green Slug Moth, *Euclea chloris*, is a pretty little moth, with its brown forewings crossed by a broad green band. The caterpillar is equally attractive, for it is red, with four black lines on the back, and the spines are yellowish.

CLEARWINGED MOTHS—THEY LOOK LIKE BEES OR FLIES

Small, but very attractive, these moths (family Aegeriidae) resemble bees, wasps, or flies. Their slender wings are very often transparent, the legs and abdomen brightly scaled in red, yellow, blue, or black. The moths fly in the daytime, with a rapid circling flight, and as they come near, you instinctively duck, so well do they remind you of angry wasps. This is another case of the protective mimicry described earlier.

The caterpillars, so far as is known, are borers in plants. Some species prefer the succulent tissues of herbaceous plants; others attack the harder wood of trees and shrubs. Their boring habit makes this a family of great economic importance, for many of the species attack plants in which man is interested.

The Squash-vine Borer, *Melittia satyriniformis,* is one of the most beautiful pests. With its metallic-green forewings, and transparent rear wings, its red abdomen and red legs fringed with black, this striking moth may be seen hovering around almost any member of the melon family. It seems to prefer squash and pumpkins. The red eggs are placed singly near the roots of the plants. When hatched, the little grub bores into the centre of the vine stem, then follows along the stem, feeding on the tender inside tissue. The plant begins to show the effects of this disturbance by a wilting of the leaves. When fully fed, and about an inch long, the caterpillar leaves the plant and burrows into the ground, spinning a rough cocoon to which particles of carth adhere. The moths emerge the next summer, in late June or early July. In the North of the United States this moth produces a single brood; in the South it is double brooded.

The Peach-tree Borer Moth, *Conopia exitiosa,* is another member of this family that is much too fond of the plants cultivated by man for his own use. The most conservative estimate of damage caused by the peach-tree borer is set at the unbelievable figure of $6,000,000 a year. With the planting of large peach orchards and the springing up of thousands of trees from tossed-away peach pits, the insect has increased tremendously in number. Originally the larvae fed upon the wild cherry and plum trees.

The adults are small but attractive moths with a wing-span of a little more than an inch. In the male, the wings are transparent, with blue edges and blue veins. Its body is blue, each segment banded with fine white or yellow lines. In the female, only the rear wings are transparent; the forewings and abdomen are steel blue, except for the fourth segment of the abdomen, which is vivid orange-red. Strange to say, however, in specimens from southern U.S.A. it is the fifth segment that is so gaily decorated.

The female lays her tiny, pretty eggs, four or five hundred of them, scattered a few here and a few there, in crevices of the bark, usually near the base of the trees selected. The larvae bore in and then feed just under the bark, going up or down. Signs of attack can be detected by the oozing sap, which thickens into the peach gum which children are so fond of chewing.

"MICROS"—THE SMALLEST MOTHS

For everyday, non-scientific purposes, we are apt to divide the Lepidoptera into two groups. Into one we place all the beautiful, graceful, showy creatures, usually large and always charming, that hover over flowers in the daytime or are attracted to lighted windows at night. Into another group go the Clothes Moths and all the other small, fuzzy, dizzy little demons, dull-coloured, inconspicuous, and unattractive pests.

Even the scientist finds it easier to separate the little fellows for concentrated study. He has dignified his surrender to convenience by calling the small moths a long name, microlepidoptera, which he usually shortens to "micros". There are at least seventy families in this group. There are probably thousands of species, many of them as yet unidentified. They are the most difficult to study, the least known, and doubtless the most interesting of all their order.

Micros are all moths, all active during the evening and at night, flying in the daytime only when disturbed—for example, when shaken out of your coat. The smallest are only a fifth of an inch in length. The largest have a wing expanse of one inch.

Under a lens, many of these creatures show great beauty. The wings which look so dull to the unaided eye are actually brightly patterned with metallic spots and lines. Sometimes the wings are oddly shaped. Those of the Plume Moth are divided so that they look like outstretched feathers. Using the lens, you will see that the moth often wears a lovely headdress, has large, bright eyes, fancy mouth appendages, and long, delicate antennae.

The Yucca Moth, Gardener and Conservationist. On the plains and mesas of the south-western United States and in many of their cultivated gardens, the Spanish bayonet or yucca lifts tall stalks of heavy, fragrant blossoms. Shake some of these flowers and watch a few very small, pale moths drop out and take off on the aimless, wiggle-waggle flight that characterizes the micros.

In one habit, however, the yucca micro is quite different from most of the group. The female gathers pollen in its mouth, which is

Jerome Wexler

A WONDERFUL STRUCTURE—TO THE TENT CATERPILLAR

Tent caterpillars construct their unsightly webs only in the spring, placing them in the crotch of branches. They are partial to apple, pear and wild cherry trees but will take up residence in others, especially if their favourites in a particular area have become thoroughly infested. While only a few species of this world-wide family inhabit North America, these are extremely populous and include some of the most destructive varieties. The adult stage is represented by a small brown moth. The females may lay as many as 300 eggs in a mass which completely encircles a twig of the food tree, and the pests pass the winter in the egg stage. One effective method of control is to seek out and destroy these egg masses. The chief natural enemy of the tent caterpillar is the larva of the caterpillar hunter beetle. See *page 1941*.

FAMILIAR CROP ROBBER

As corn is a standard item for the average home gardener in America, as well as an extensively grown staple crop, the corn earworm is found almost everywhere. Together with the closely related European corn borers which became established near Boston about 1917, these caterpillars destroy millions of dollars worth of corn each year. They feed on other garden crops and also on wild plants, which makes control difficult. The moths of both species are small, rather inconspicuous yellow creatures. *See page 1950.*

H. J. Brigance

KEY FIGURE IN A FABULOUS INDUSTRY

According to legend, some 4,000 years ago the Chinese Empress Si-Ling accidentally dropped a silkworm cocoon into a cup of hot tea. Retrieving it, she discovered it could be unwound in one long thread of strong, lustrous fibre, and experimented with weaving some of this thread: the silk industry had its beginning. Silk is known in China as "Si" in her honour. The thread as spun by the caterpillar varies in diameter so that of approximately 4,000 yards of silk on each cocoon only from 300 to 1,000 yards can be used commercially. Some 2,500 cocoons yield one pound of silk. *See page 1944.*

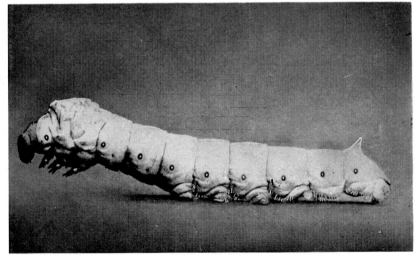

Culver Pictures, Inc.

The white-marked tussock moth takes its name from the four white tussocks of hairs on its caterpillar. These elegant caterpillars with their red heads and black and yellow striped bodies are widespread throughout eastern North America and frequently occur in such numbers as to completely strip the leaves from the trees where they cluster. It is estimated that only ten per cent reach maturity, as they are attacked not only by predatory birds but by parasites which in turn have parasites. The mature male moth is a small, drab, inconspicuous insect, and the wingless female is a fat little ash-grey creature which lives only long enough to lay the eggs. *See page 1939*

[16-1]

[16-1A]

The curious saddleback belongs to the "slug caterpillar" family, the members of which have practically no feet and slide around over the surface of the leaves on which they feed. The spines of this species are greatly to be feared as they are easily broken off and can become embedded in the flesh, causing extreme irritation. The thin cocoon is equally dangerous to handle as the spines are interwoven in the silk. The one-inch saddleback caterpillar is quite common in the eastern United States; the adult is a small, fat-bodied moth, rich brown in colour. *See page 1948*

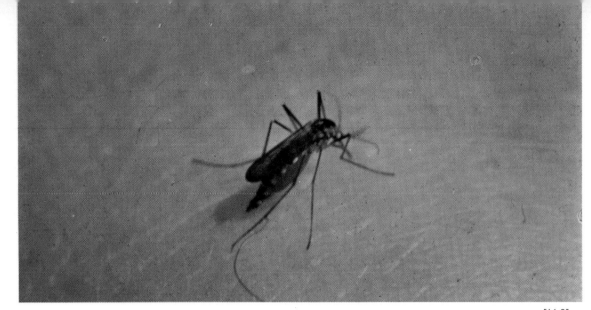

[16-2]

Mosquitoes belong to the "true" fly group, an order of insects known as Diptera. Many species of mosquitoes serve as hosts for the reproduction and development of new generations of the parasitic protozoans which cause malaria, yellow fever and other serious afflictions. Since the larvae of the various host mosquitoes generally mature during a relatively prolonged period of temperatures at least in the low 70's, these dangerous species are more or less restricted to tropical and semi-tropical regions. Mosquitoes of the temperate zones are for the most part only a nuisance. The ingenious anaesthetic-injecting, blood-sucking apparatus is the property of the "singing" female; the silent male never bites but innocuously sips plant juices.   *See page 1957*

Smallest of all the flies are the gall midges most of which measure less than one-tenth of an inch. These tiny, fragile creatures with their transparent gauzy wings are better known by their activities than by their appearance. While numerous species are beneficial, feeding on decaying vegetation or on plant lice, mites and other harmful insects, many others are serious competitors, despoiling man's carefully cultivated plants. According to species and host plant, the females lay their eggs in leaves or stems and some substance, either injected with the eggs or resulting from the growth of the larvae, causes the plant to produce a characteristic swelling or "gall". These maple bladder galls are caused by midges with a formidable scientific name almost 20 times as long as they are.   *See page 1961*

[16-2A]

specially modified for this purpose, and carefully places it on the stigma of the yucca flower, thus assuring seeds for her young. Then she deposits her eggs in the flower's ovary. The larvae feed on the seeds, always leaving some to provide for future crops.

MICROS OF ECONOMIC IMPORTANCE

With a few exceptions, like the yucca moth, only those micros have been studied whose interests conflict with man's. Among these are the three species of clothes moths that have bothered us for so long. They belong to the Tineidae family, many of whose members feed

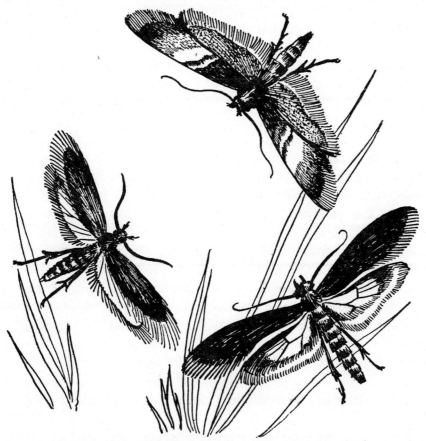

EVERY HOUSEKEEPER HATES THESE THREE CRIMINALS

There are only three kinds of common clothes moths. All have spread to the Western Hemisphere from their original Old World home. The adult moths look very much alike; the smallest has a wing-spread of about half an inch, the largest, five-eighths of an inch. The caterpillars, however, build quite different kinds of cases or cocoons. *Top:* Case-bearing clothes moth, *Trichophaga tapetzella. Bottom left:* Webbing clothes moth, *Tineola bisselliella. Bottom right:* Old-fashioned clothes moth, *Tinea pellionella.*

on dead animal matter, particularly fur, feathers, and wool; but some feed on fungi and decaying vegetation.

Leaf Miners, belonging to several families, are beautiful, bright, or metallic-coloured, moths, exquisitely shaped, whose caterpillars attack the leaves, twigs, and fruit of practically all trees and shrubs, as well as many greenhouse plants.

Leaf Rollers, not so brilliantly coloured, have small pink, yellow, or green caterpillars which feed on leaves, fruits, and nuts almost to the despair of man. To this group belong the terrible Codling Moth, the Oriental Peach Moth, the Grape Moth, the Cranberry Black-head Wireworm, and many another pest throughout the world. Here also belong the Mexican-jumping-bean Moth larvae, whose antics have delighted children for ages.

Larvae of a great many micro species feed on our dried and processed foods, on flour, meal, breakfast foods, macaroni, noodles, and the like, dried fruit, and shelled nuts. Their living adds greatly to the cost of ours.

Heroes of Australia. But in the same family, with the worst of the meal and dried-fruit moths, lives the famous Cactus Moth, *Cactoblastis cactorum*, true hero to the Australians. Years ago misguided persons introduced the American prickly-pear cactus into Australia. In an incredibly short time the cactus had covered sixty million acres of that continent's dry pasture land. In 1925 Argentina sent the suffering Australians 2,750 cactus-moth eggs. These were placed on the cactus leaves, hatched well, and the larvae burrowed in and set to work. Within the next few years, millions of moth eggs were distributed around Australia, and everywhere the larvae rapidly destroyed the cactus.

Another group of micros whose habits coincide with our desires are some species of the tiny, lovely Sun Moths. Their minute caterpillars have been observed feeding on mealy bugs, scales, and other coccids.

The great majority of the microlepidoptera are still unknown to us. As we learn more about them, we shall doubtless find many that we can call beneficial, because they feed on something that we want destroyed.

The True Flies—Biters, Scavengers, and Poisoners

AMONG English-speaking people, almost any insect that has noticeable wings, or one that makes much use of its wings, is called a fly, or some special kind of fly. So we have Butterflies, Dragonflies, Fireflies, Harvest Flies, and May Flies, as well as Houseflies, Bluebottle Flies, and Horseflies. Actually, only the last three named belong to the "true" flies (order Diptera). As we think about these for a moment, we may recall other only too familiar insects that are also true flies: Mosquitoes, Midges, Robber Flies, Fruit Flies, and many more.

HOW TRUE FLIES DIFFER FROM OTHER INSECTS

Look carefully at an assortment of these various flies, and you will see that they have one prominent characteristic in common: each has only one pair of wings. All other insects have either no wings at all or two pairs.

What has happened to the second pair of wings in the Diptera? Just behind the base of their wings you can see a pair of curious little knobs, mounted on slender stalks. These odd structures are called "halteres", or balancers. Since they occupy the approximate position where the second pair of wings would be, if present, and since they vibrate when the flies are flying, it is assumed by many insect experts that they are modified wings. Other entomologists believe that the halteres may be a more recent, and perhaps independent, development, appearing after the second pair of wings had ceased to function, had grown smaller and smaller, and had eventually disappeared.

It is this single pair of wings and the halteres that distinguish the Diptera from all other insects. They have one other noticeable characteristic—large eyes, sometimes occupying most of the head. In general, members of the Diptera do not differ as widely from one another as do the members of some other orders. Therefore we consider the Diptera as being homogeneous, meaning that its members have very similar characteristics, as distinguished from the Hemiptera, which is a heterogeneous order (having widely varying members).

FLIES ARE ABUNDANT EVERYWHERE

Flies make their homes everywhere, from the lands of long winters and short summers to the steamiest jungles. Some are small, nearly invisible; others are large. Some are very dull in appearance; others dress brilliantly in yellows, greens, and reds. Some are beneficial to man as scavengers, or in their parasitic attacks upon other insects.

Others, however, are veritable demons, assailing you frontally as well as from both quarters and the rear. These little devils may be plain biters, leaving painful, but temporary, reminders of their presence. Or they may be insidious injectors of protozoans that will leave you suffering from dangerous diseases. Totalling up, however, the flies are probably more beneficial than dangerous to man's interests. The grubs of some species of flies are used as food by a number of primitive peoples.

Although the Diptera are not as numerous in species as the Lepidoptera or the Coleoptera, some seventy-three thousand have been described, and new ones are constantly being added to our lists.

CRANE FLIES—SUMMER DANCERS

At about sunset on a hot summer day, invite yourself to a dance of the crane flies. For an excellent view, take your seat near the top of a grassy bank above a marsh or pond. Even if such a location is not at hand, many such dances will be going on over wet meadows or at the opening of a small ravine.

Up and down, up and down, fragilely and clumsily, the crane flies dance until night falls, sometimes hundreds joining in the delicate rhythm. These are all males, and usually all of one species, although occasionally a straggler of some other kind will join in the gaieties. The dance is apparently a kind of courting entertainment, with the lady flies watching quietly from the side lines.

The crane flies (family Tipulidae) are easily recognized by their long, slender wings and bodies, but particularly by their very long legs. Sometimes they are called daddy long legs, a name used in America for the long-legged spiders or harvestmen to which it is more generally applied.

The Tipulidae are weak fliers, their second and third pairs of legs dragging out behind, while the first pair is held doubled up in front. Once you have seen their curious flying appearance you will always be able to recognize it.

COLLECTING CRANE FLIES

Since they get about so clumsily, you will find the crane flies easy to catch. However, few entomologists have bothered to collect them because they are so difficult to mount and keep. Some of the legs are sure to be lost. The safest method is to pin each specimen as soon as you catch it; if this is not possible, place each in a separate paper envelope. Pinned and dried specimens are still more fragile, and it is seldom that you see a perfect example in a collection.

CRANE FLIES AROUND THE WORLD

Contrary to the usual geographical variation seen in insects, the crane flies of the tropics are commonly smaller than those in the cooler climates. Note, however, a rule-proving exception, the Snow Fly, which is only about a sixth of an inch long and is found in such cold regions as northern Canada and also in high altitudes.

The warmer temperate regions produce some truly enormous crane flies. China and Australia have the largest, but the author has seen several in the United States whose outspread legs would cover a small saucer. They look like giant mosquitoes. Every once in a while one of these large crane flies is brought into the author's office in New York City, usually in a milk bottle, its proud possessor certain that he has captured a dangerous New Jersey mosquito.

We are fortunate that crane flies cannot bite. If they could, they would undoubtedly be dangerous to have about. A few are pests, feeding on cultivated crops. Most of the species feed on vegetation growing in swampy areas.

Crane-fly larvae have cylindrical, grublike bodies, the largest over two inches long, protected by a body wall or integument so tough that

they are often called "leatherjackets". Many live in the decaying
vegetation in swamps, or in the humus of thick, damp woods, and
quite a few are aquatic or semi-aquatic. The larvae of some species in
Europe feed on root vegetables and bulbs. The larvae of another are
something of a pest to California grain crops.

Various Crane Flies. More than six thousand species have been
described. One-third of these have been named by one man, Dr. C. P.
Alexander, of Amherst, Mass. As a result of his energetic efforts, our

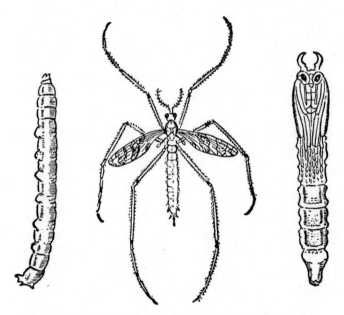

THE LONG-LEGGED CRANE FLY AND ITS FORERUNNERS

Sometimes a host of crane flies can be seen dancing together over a warm wet meadow.
They look like giant mosquitoes, but they cannot bite, and the legs of some species may
be two inches long. The larva or grub (*left*) has such a tough covering that it is called a
"leather jacket". It lives in wet ground or muddy streams or in decaying wood. The pupa
(*right*) looks like a miniature totem pole.

knowledge of the crane flies has been far advanced, and new species
are constantly being listed. Any collection of crane flies from a little-
studied region will yield new members.

A few species are wingless, or have wings reduced to little wingless
pads. One of these is the tiny snow fly, or snow gnat, *Chionea valga*,
of the northern United States and Canada. In 1946 the author took
two specimens of a wingless species that were clinging to the vegetation

along a roadside ditch in the mountains overlooking Mexico City, at an altitude of twelve thousand feet.

A very pretty species, *Bittacomorpha clavipes*, black, with white bands all around the legs, has its legs thickly covered with very short, fine hairs. It is practically invisible when it flies, looking like an ethereal fluff of down. It has been called the phantom crane fly.

THE MOTH FLY

The attractive little moth fly is so called because its body, legs, wings, and antennae are densely clothed with fine hairs, making it look like a tiny moth. The moth flies are so small, seldom over one sixth of an inch in length, that they would scarcely be noticed except for their habit of flying to a window and there walking back and forth, spreading and folding their wings as they walk. Their wings are bent at a sharp angle at the base and lie rooflike over the body when the insects are at rest. This also adds to the mothlike appearance of these flies.

The moth fly's wormlike larvae live in decaying vegetation, fungi, sewage, and dung, and sometimes in flowing water. The adults can be found crawling or flying around.

This family (Psychodidae) is a small one, and, except for one genus, is rather beneficial to man, since its larvae assist in the disintegration of decayed animal and vegetable matter. The exception is the dreaded *Phlebotomus*, a bloodsucking genus, most species of which transmit disease. One of these carries an infectious skin ailment, the dangerous verruga disease, prevalent on the western slopes of the Peruvian Andes. Others transmit kala azar and the Oriental sore in Asiatic countries.

Phlebotomus flies have longer legs than the other moth flies and are less hairy. They fly only at night, hiding in dark caves or rocky crevices during the day. After their habit of night flying was discovered, the Peruvian government was able to reduce verruga mortality greatly by carefully screening village and railroad-camp sleeping quarters. The newer insect repellents should also serve to ward off the attacks of these flies.

THE MOSQUITO—CARRIER OF DREAD DISEASE

Of all the insects, the mosquito (family Culicidae) undoubtedly causes the most suffering, both to humans and to animals. Not only do mosquitoes disturb and annoy us with their persistent biting, but many species act as distributors for some of our most dangerous diseases.

Malaria, yellow fever, dengue, encephalomyelitis, filariasis, and other afflictions result from the microscopic protozoans which spend

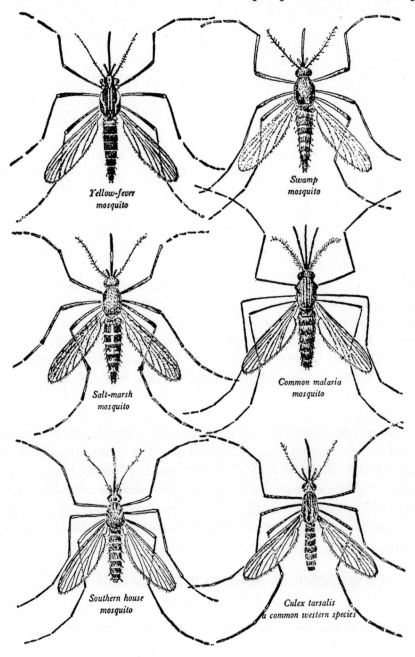

Yellow-fever mosquito

Swamp mosquito

Salt-marsh mosquito

Common malaria mosquito

Southern house mosquito

Culex tarsalis a common western species

part of their existence as harmful parasites in man or animals, another part, non-injuriously, in mosquitoes, and a third part, again harmfully, in a host similar to the first. The slightest bite of a mosquito carrying a supply of germs acquired from some individual already suffering from one of these diseases is sufficient to start a new case.

We all think we are familiar with mosquitoes, but only when we have closely examined one or more species under a good microscope do we realize how beautiful they are.

Even the beak of the female, for only the female bites, is an exquisite apparatus, more perfect than any man-made instrument for the same purpose could be. The feathery antennae of the males are lovely in the extreme. The wings are decorated with scales fastened to the veins in a very exact manner that differs with each species. The bodies are also covered with scales, each species having its characteristic design.

The larvae are water animals, each kind living under certain particular conditions, which are as varied as the number of species.

PHANTOM GNATS—ALMOST INVISIBLE

A little-known family of flies, closely related to the mosquitoes and formerly placed in their family, the phantom gnats (family Chaoboridae) differ, however, in having no scales on the wings or body. The missing scales are usually replaced by very minute hairs. These flies also are unable to bite.

The Chaoboridae are a group of insects helpful to mankind, because their larvae feed upon mosquito larvae. They also attack the young of other insects, and if these are scarce may become cannibalistic.

The larvae, although abundant at times, are not often noticed because they are so transparent as to be almost invisible, this being the reason for calling these insects "phantom gnats". They can occasionally be seen in quiet, shady pools, where your eye may be caught by the one or two airlike bubbles in their lucid bodies, and then by their dark eyes.

In some tropical regions, phantom gnats are so plentiful that they are strained from pools, pressed dry, and thus preserved for food.

MIDGES—SMALL BUT IMPORTANT

The midges are a large family of fragile, frequently minute, mosquito-like flies (Chironomidae). They usually occur in numbers along the borders of ponds and streams, for it is in the water that these insects, as larvae and pupae, have spent most of their lives. A few species, however, are not water-dwellers, but live in damp, decaying vegetation or wet, humus-filled soil.

The water-dwelling midges are one of the principal sources of food for small fishes, a fact for the fisherman to remember, as he curses and flails at the "pesky critters". Midge larvae are soft and wormlike and spend their hours burrowing in the oozy muck. Some are called blood-worms because they possess a haemoglobin which gives them a blood-red colour. Those that live among water weeds are usually greenish.

It is usually on a warm summer evening that the pupa swims to the surface, its skin breaks open, and out crawls the adult midge. So many emerge during favourable seasons that vast hordes of them drift out over the land. Many are carried by the winds far from the water, never to be able to return to deposit their eggs. Most midges cannot bite, but by the numbers that lodge in hair, eyes, nose, and mouth, they can make one very uncomfortable.

Many a householder along the Great Lakes, delighting at day's end in his newly painted home, has awakened the next morning to find thousands of these little flies firmly embedded in the sticky paint. Street lights are sometimes capped with a crown of midges mixed with May flies, and office buildings may be draped with mantles of midges over their windward walls.

When examined closely, adult midges show up as attractive insects, with their long, slender legs, delicate wings, and especially the large, feathery antennae of the males.

Sand Flies, Punkies, and No-see-ums. Although it is true that most midges cannot bite, one small group belonging to the genus *Culicoides* more than makes up for what the others lack in this respect. These are the sand flies, punkies, and no-see-ums of the northern United States and Canada. You can scarcely see them, but you can certainly feel them, for it is their business to bite the moment they alight on your skin. Their bite feels like the jab of a red-hot needle.

The sand flies generally fly just at dusk or on muggy, overcast days. Since they are so small, they can pass through the average mosquito-proof screen.

Before the days of DDT, cottages located along waterways of swampy areas were regularly invaded by the no-see-ums every evening.

Now, by spraying all screens with a 5 per cent DDT oil spray, the biggest percentage of these flies are killed as they pass through the mesh.

GALL MIDGES

The gall midges are better known by their activities than by their appearance, because they are such tiny, fragile creatures. The smallest of all the flies, most of them are less than one-tenth of an inch long. Only a lens can reveal their delicate beauty. Hairy, long-legged, and equipped with long, beaded antennae, they fly about on transparent, gauzy wings. Their feeding habits are varied, and perhaps it is easiest to consider them from this angle. They belong to the family Cecidomyiidae.

The predatory species all fit in nicely with human needs, feeding upon plant lice, mites, coccids, and bark beetles.

A good number are saprophagous; that is, they feed upon decaying vegetation, dead trees, fungi, and dung. They are beneficial as scavengers, returning organic matter to a condition in which it can be reabsorbed by plants.

A great many gall midges are phytophagous; that is, they feed on living plant tissue. This makes them man's competitors, particularly when they attack plants which he has been cultivating.

The Hessian Fly, *Phytophaga destructor*, is a species belonging to the phytophagous group. As a destroyer of wheat it has few equals; its annual damage is estimated at nearly $100,000,000. The Hessian fly does not confine its attentions to wheat; it is just as fond of rye and barley. The eggs are laid along the stem; the hatching larvae, protected under the leaf sheath, feed on the stem, injuring or killing the plant. Since there are two or three generations a year, tremendous destruction results.

The Hessian fly is believed to have originated in Asia, spreading to Europe in hay or cereals. It reached Long Island in the Revolutionary War, carried there in straw that the Hessian soldiers brought for bedding. By 1884 it had reached the Pacific coast, having travelled from wheat field to wheat field as the American settlers pushed farther and farther West.

Other Midges. Another wheat pest, the Wheat Midge, *Diplosis tritici*, was also imported from Europe, a short while after the Hessian fly. The Pear Midge, *Contarinia pyrivora*, enters the pear fruit through the blossom. It causes a lumpy development in the fruit, particularly around the core. It also emigrated from Europe.

Many of America's destructive pests arrived from Europe years ago, before the establishment of the United States Bureau of Entomology and Plant Quarantine. Since this important government agency was set up and developed its thorough inspection of all plant material and other possible sources of infestation, fewer pests are able to reach America's shores. Nevertheless, in spite of this careful inspection, some foreign insects and plants still get established within them. Many never becomes pests; but there are always a few that, having left their natural controls behind, or finding conditions there favourable for their development, quickly spread until they became serious problems.

Many of the phytophagous cecidomyiids produce galls, those curious enlargements of the plant tissues. They attack the roots, stems, leaves, and flowers, showing particular interest in the plants belonging to the families Gramineae, the grains; Salicaceae, the willows; and Compositae, the chrysanthemums, daisies, sunflowers, and the like.

BLACK FLIES—SOME ARE BRILLIANTLY TINTED

Everyone who has vacationed in the North Woods has suffered from these stout, humpbacked, short-legged flies. Toward evening, or on overcast days, the female black fly, for it is only she who bites, starts her search for a possible victim. Noiselessly, she sneaks up on you and jabs you viciously on any exposed part, but preferably on the back of the hands or neck. A small blood blister is the visible result of the bite, but an intense itching is felt at the spot for hours.

These flies are bothersome not only in the North, but in the tropics as well. During a recent trip in eastern Peru, the author was troubled greatly just at dusk by swarms of black flies. One of the newly developed insect repellents was effective against mosquitoes but failed to ward off the simuliids unless the exposed skin was thoroughly doused.

Although most of the black flies do not cause any trouble other than their severe bites, a few are carriers of disease. *Eusimulium damnosum*, widely distributed in parts of Africa, transmits to man the Round-worm, *Onchocera volvulus*, which builds painful cysts under its victim's skin, especially in the eyes. There have been occasions when animals, both wild and domestic, and poultry, have died in numbers as a result of diseases carried by various species of these flies.

While many of the black flies are true to their colour name, some are more brightly tinted with yellow, orange, and red. They have a number of other common names, such as buffalo gnat and turkey gnat. Only about three hundred species make up this family (Simuliidae), but, as is frequently the case when a group is limited in species, it more than compensates for this lack by the multitudes of its individuals.

Some Well-known Black Flies. The most widely distributed species in America, is named *Simulium vittatum*. A rather pretty species, called the White-stockinged Black Fly, *Simulium venustum*, because portions of the leg are marked with white, is also widely distributed east of the Rocky Mountains and as far north as Alaska. The Adirondack Black Fly, *Prosimulium hirtipes*, is found in the Adirondacks and northeastern states. The Yellow Gnat, *Prosimulium fulvum*, is a bad pest in the western states.

A black fly which attacks turkeys as well as domestic animals and man throughout the southern part of the United States is *Simulium meriodionale*.

INTERESTING WAYS OF BLACK-FLY LARVAE AND PUPAE

The larvae and pupae of the black fly lead interesting lives. The larvae inhabit swift flowing streams, clinging in groups to silken threads fastened to the rocks on the bottom. Sometimes they are so numerous as to make a black patch, looking almost like algae, covering square yards of the stream bed.

Here they feed on the life that the rushing water brings them, sweeping it in with brushes on their heads. Each tiny larva clings by a sucker-like process on the end of its abdomen to the silken thread it is constantly spinning. If disturbed it will let go its hold, but will not be washed away, because it has many other threads in the vicinity or can very rapidly spin a new thread, first having it very securely anchored.

When mature, the larva constructs a tiny, silken nest in which to pupate. At first it is completely enclosed in this cocoon. When the larva has changed to a pupa, the downstream end is pushed out of the nest, making a convenient exit for what is about to be created. The pupa rests, with its fore part projecting into the stream, breathing the air from the well-aerated water, awaiting the day of its liberation.

Slowly, the pupal skin becomes inflated as air is filtered from the insect into the space just under the skin. The skin becomes rounded and buoyant. Rounded and more rounded, buoyant and more buoyant it grows, until this tiny pupal balloon pops from its nest and soars to the surface of the water, where it breaks open, releasing the fully developed, winged fly.

GADFLIES AND HORSEFLIES

Members of this family (Tabanidae) are mostly large, husky flies that announce their arrival by a loud "whir-r-r-r" as they circle their intended victim. One group, however, is more subtle, informing you of its presence only by a vicious jab on the back of the neck or some other vulnerable spot. These sneak attackers are smaller than most of their relatives. They belong to the genus *Chrysops*, and are popularly called gadflies, deer flies, clegs, breezes, or ear flies.

The *Chrysops* tend to have yellowish abdomens streaked with darker lines or blotches. A few have dark, or even black, abdomens. Their clear wings are usually marked with one or more dark bands or spots.

Normally they live in the woodland places, where they attack all mammals, large and small, from rabbits to deer. They particularly relish human blood, as any hunter or fisherman can tell you. It is believed that some of the western *Chrysops* may transmit tularemia to persons. As with the mosquitoes and many other Diptera, it is the female that bites.

The genus *Tabanus* contains the larger, noisier species which are the true horseflies. Some are also called greenheads because of their very large, iridescent eyes, streaked with shooting lines of red, yellow, blue, and green. The eyes occupy most of the head, particularly in the males; you cannot help admiring the beauty of the greenheads, while despising the way they make their living.

TORMENTORS OF DOMESTIC ANIMALS

Tabanus species frequent pastures and more open country, where they prey upon horses, cattle, and other domestic animals. It is not at all uncommon to see open sores made by these flies about the neck, legs, and backs of domestic stock. The sores develop because the flies return again and again to feed in the same spot, always an area out of reach of the lashing tail and questing head. If the flies are numerous enough, as they often are, you can see the poor animals rushing frantically around pasture or pen to escape their tormentors.

DEER FLY, HOUSEFLY, AND HORSEFLY—PESTS TO MAN AND BEAST

Flies are attractive little insects in this picture, but their habits do not please us. The prettily marked deer fly (*top left*) attacks all mammals, and is thought to transmit tularemia to people. We are always fighting the housefly (*bottom left*) but it still survives, partly because it can produce many generations in one summer. The horsefly (*right*) is usually large, with enormous brilliant green eyes. Not only does this pest drive animals frantic— it also transmits anthrax.

The damage done by the horseflies is not limited to mere sores. They also frequently transmit anthrax, an infectious disease often attacking cattle and sheep, and sometimes man, and also the trypanosomes that cause the surra disease in horses.

SEA-GOING HORSEFLIES

Even though the horsefly is known as a pasture and meadow insect, a number of species of *Tabanus* leave the land to venture far out to sea. The author has seen them miles from shore on the Great Lakes, as well as incredibly far out on the Atlantic and Pacific oceans.

Seemingly, they come from nowhere to settle in sheltered places on a ship. After a short rest there, they sally forth to attack. One wonders where all these flies could come from.

The explanation that comes first to mind is that they stowed away on the ship before it left port. This is doubtless true in many cases; but vessels that have been thoroughly inspected and found free of flies at the start, very quickly begin to pick up a sizeable quota. This seems to demonstrate that the flies are on the wing over the water. Since they are strong fliers, many may have flown away from land. Many more are carried to sea by strong winds. A passing ship can provide a welcome resting place for these tired insects. Undoubtedly, many flies, like butterflies flying over the oceans, settle on floating debris.

Other Black Flies. If you see a large, black horsefly with smoky wings, in the eastern United States, it is pretty certain to be *Tabanus atratus*.

If you see a similar fly in the West, it is probably *punctifer*. These two are among the largest of the horseflies.

About 2,500 species of the Tabanidae family have been described, some three hundred of these being distributed throughout North America. They appear in every climate, although more commonly in the warmer countries, and at high altitudes as well as in the lowlands, but nearly always around water or damp places, because their larvae almost always live in the water or in mud. The eggs are long and slender and are laid in overlapping layers in masses attached to the foliage along the stream banks or in swampy places. As soon as they are hatched, the little larvae drop into the wet muck where they spend nearly a year feeding and growing.

BEE FLIES—THEY LOOK LIKE BUMBLEBEES

When you walk along a sunny woodland pathway during late summer you are almost certain to see and hear one of the bee flies hovering

This greatly enlarged photograph of the well-known fruit fly, Drosophila, clearly shows the distinguishing characteristics of the order Diptera. These flies have a single pair of wings whereas all other insects have either two pairs or none at all. They also have a pair of curious little knobs on spines, called "halteres" or "balancers", which occupy the approximate position of a second pair of wings. The large eyes give the appearance of being attached to the head rather than set into it. As each female lays up to 200 eggs and the entire life cycle of these creatures is completed in 10 days at temperatures of 80 degrees Fahrenheit, Drosophila occupies a very important place in laboratory studies of genetics and, more recently, hereditary effects of exposure to radiation. *See page 1953*

[16-3]

[16-3A]

The literature of Ptolemaic Egypt refers to the syrphid flies as "ox-born bees" and prescribes elaborate rituals for their spontaneous generation from the carcasses of dead oxen. It is a point of curiosity that this belief persisted throughout the ancient world in spite of the fact that the "proof of the pudding"—no honey—must have been obvious. The larvae of some species, like those of many flies, live and pupate in decaying flesh. Syrphids are also known as flower or hover flies because when they are not resting on flowers feeding on the pollen, they may be seen hovering on rapidly vibrating wings about eight to twelve feet above the ground. *See page 1972*

The bluebottle fly or blowfly belongs to the same family as the common housefly which it closely resembles. The several species of bluebottle flies usually hatch within 24 hours although sometimes they hatch in the mother's body and she deposits the living larvae. Their principal food is carrion but they breed in all types of offensive material. The family as a whole was probably associated with man long before he had acquired and domesticated animals. Some species aggravate their pest-status by biting, but all are a serious menace to the health of mankind as they visit, indiscriminately, kitchens, dining rooms and disease-contaminated refuse.

See page 1980

[16-4]

[16-4A]

The ichneumon fly is really a wasp. The large number of species of this insect-destroying insect differ in size but in general they very closely resemble one another. The females have a long ovipositor, the tip of which is fitted with tiny teeth for drilling into solid wood. They somehow locate wood-boring larvae in tree trunks and branches and drill through to the burrows where they deposit their eggs. Upon hatching, the ichneumon larvae feed on the wood borers. Some species are parasitic upon various moth caterpillars and cocoons, but the family as a whole probably destroys as many useful insects as harmful ones.

See page 1989

There are some 2,500 species of ants, and the black carpenter ants which are found in temperate regions the world over are among the largest. They burrow in dead logs and house timbers and can be extremely destructive if allowed to spread. They sometimes establish a colony in the heartwood of a living tree and eradicating them without killing the tree is very difficult. All the species of ants are social insects, living and working together with a degree of organization which is amazing. The workers are imperfectly developed females. They construct the nest and keep it clean, and care for the eggs, larvae and cocoons. The carpenter ants have a soldier caste of large workers which defend the colony.

See page 1994

[16-5]

[16-5A]

The queen ants and the much smaller males have wings. On a certain day all the colonies of a certain species for miles around will drive out the winged individuals which mate in flight. After mating they all drop to the ground where the males quickly die or are eaten by birds or mammals. Each female tears off her wings and seeks a place to establish a new colony. She constructs a small chamber and lays a few eggs which she tends herself until a small nucleus of workers has developed. These then take over the active duties of the nest and from this time on the queen is simply an egg-laying machine. *See page 1992*

The nest of the white-faced or bald-faced hornet is started in the spring by a single queen and reaches its full size, usually larger than a football, by autumn. The paper-making wasps use wood fibre from weathered fences, buildings and dead trees to construct their nests. The wood is chewed and mixed with saliva to form a pulp which is then spread out layer by layer. The interior of the nest is divided into connected chambers and some are large enough to accommodate 10,000 hornets. The entire colony, except for a number of young mated queens which hibernate, dies at the first severe frost.

See page 2004

[16-6]

[16-6A]

A few species of wasps are solitary, but most of them live in colonies although they are not genuinely socially inclined as are the ants and some bees. The nests vary with the species, not only in size and shape but also in location and materials used in their construction. Some wasps use mud, others clay, and there is a cuckoo wasp which lays its eggs in other wasps' nests. The common paper wasps build an unprotected nest but usually select a site which affords more shelter than a clump of grass. Many species sting but do not kill insects which they then seal into each cell with the egg to provide food for the larva. The common paper wasps do not place food in their nests but feed the larvae daily until they pupate.

See page 2004

close to the ground, its bright wings buzzing noisily. At first sight and sound, you may think it is a bumblebee.

It is a fuzzy fly, however, its largish abdomen decorated with short, thickset hairs which may be yellow, orange, white, black, or even a combination of several of these colours. The transparent wings are blotched with black in patterns peculiar to each species. Some species sport a long proboscis sticking straight out in front.

Their hovering will identify the bee flies more quickly than any description can; for, on wings vibrating so rapidly as to be nearly invisible, they remain absolutely fixed over a spot. Suddenly, with wings still vibrating, they dart off to hover over another spot a few feet away. Even in cities, above scorching pavements, one may see bee flies hovering.

FEEDING AND MATING

The adults eat pollen or sip nectar from flowers, but the larvae are parasitic on other insects. The newly hatched little maggot hunts energetically for a bee's nest, the egg mass of a grasshopper, a caterpillar, a beetle grub, or whatever that particular bee-fly species prefers. The parent bee fly, of course, drops her eggs as close as possible to the preferred host. If successful in its search, the larva settles down to feed and does not move again.

In this family (Bombyliidae), about two thousand species have been described so far. One of the largest of them, *Bombylius major*, is also one of the most common and one of the most widely distributed in the Northern Hemisphere. It is densely covered with black, white, and brown hairs, and the front halves of its wings are black. It is parasitic on the larvae of some of the bees. The history of another member of this family, the Anthrax Fly, also parasitic on bees, has been beautifully told by the great French writer, Henri Fabre. In compensation, to man, at least, for the family depredation on bees, several African species are parasitic on the pupae of the Tsetse Fly.

ROBBER FLIES—HEAVILY ARMED INSECT HIGHWAYMEN

All insects, except the very largest, fall easy prey to that swooping highwayman the robber fly. Even the honeybees, wasps, and the smaller bumblebees, armed though they are with powerful stingers, are no match for a robber fly and its paralysing proboscis.

EAL / 16—C

Swift of flight, this fly overtakes its victim in the air and clutches it with all six powerful legs; at the same time the fly jabs its beak into the victim. Almost instantly the struggles cease, and the robber fly carries the body to some convenient perch to suck it dry.

Only a violent disturbance can force the fly to drop its food before the last drop has been drained. A slight disturbance will only cause it to carry the carcass off to a quieter spot. The wanderer afield is certain sooner or later to see one of the robber flies in action.

ROBBER FLIES AND THE BEES

Beekeepers are likely to fear robber flies, or assassin flies, as they are sometimes called, because of the destruction they are thought to cause in beehives. This is a questionable fear, because it would take a great many flies to make any considerable inroad into the population of even a single hive, and robber flies never appear to be very numerous. In queen-bee rearing yards the damage might become serious through the destruction of valuable queens.

HANDLE WITH CARE!

To the would-be collector of robber flies, a warning must be issued. Before the author learned to handle them, two species of this fly bit him every time he tried to take them out of his net. If the fly can get into the proper position, it loves to sink its beak into the ball of your thumb, creating a painful wound. Of course, one can bear this fly no ill-will, since it is acting purely in self-defence. If you are hesitant about experiencing a robber-fly bite, try to steer these flies into your killing bottle instead of seizing them in your fingers.

The larvae are also predatory, feeding upon insects and perhaps other small, soft-bodied creatures living in rotten wood, decaying leaf mould, or other vegetable debris.

The family (Asilidae) is a large one, with over four thousand species widely distributed throughout the world A few of the species are quite small, but most of them are fairly large. One of the largest, an Australian species, *Phellus glaucus*, is over two inches long, with a wing-span of three and a half inches. It is steel blue in colour. A smaller species, but perhaps the handsomest of all robber flies, also lives in Australia. It is *Blepharotes coriareus*, blackish in colour, except for the abdomen, which is a brilliant orange, decorated with tufts of black and white hairs; it has smoky-grey wings.

ROBBER FLIES OF THE UNITED STATES

In the United States, there are three general styles of body design in the asilids. In the genus *Leptogaster*, represented by only a few species, the abdomen is elongated, with the last three segments much enlarged, giving the fly a wasplike appearance. In *Erax* and *Asilus*, to which most of the species belong, the reverse is true. Here, the abdomen is quite thick at the base, tapering toward the tip. In the male, the extreme tip

ROBBER FLIES—ASSASSINS IN THE AIR

Black, brown, or reddish insects, usually covered with bristles, these husky brigands can kill even wasps and bumblebees on the wing, for they are very fast, very strong, and big (some are two inches long). Their larvae live in rotten wood or vegetation, feeding on the larvae of other insects. Robber flies are found in open, sunny fields.

is rounded and slightly upturned. The female, however, has a tip that tapers to a very sharp end. She uses this tip to insert her eggs into rotting vegetation or old logs.

The third style, illustrated by the genus *Dasyllis*, has a rounded abdomen which, together with the head and thorax, is covered with a dense cloak of hairs. This plumage is usually gold and black, giving the flies the appearance of bumblebees. Perhaps this resemblance to bumblebees enables the robber flies to get close to their victims. Or it may protect the flies from other predatory creatures which mistake it for a stinging insect.

It is also possible that this resemblance may just have happened. There are many examples of mimicry throughout the insect world which to our human eyes seem to serve a definite purpose, but we have no reason to believe that insects see things as we do, or that they would come to the same conclusions about them.

MYDAS FLIES—LARGE AND SPECTACULAR

The family Mydaidae is a small one as far as species are concerned, and would be omitted from a general book of this sort, except for the large and spectacular insects it contains.

Mydas clavatus is the only species found in the northern and eastern parts of the United States. It is velvety black with smoky wings. For contrast, it wears a brilliant orange-red band on the second basal segment of its abdomen Its wing expanse of two inches gives it plenty of power and speed and the capacity to create a startling noise when it suddenly zooms across one's path on a hot, sleepy afternoon.

A DISAPPEARING INSECT

The author first saw one of these flies during his boyhood. It was basking in the sunshine on a dead beech-snag standing in a dense growth of blackberries, poison ivy, and young sassafras. Carefully he approached the lovely creature, breathlessly reaching out his net to capture it.

But the job was bungled, and the fly was gone!

Thinking there might be others around, the writer waited eagerly, with his eyes glued to the beech trunk. Five minutes, ten, twenty, passed. The spot of sunshine was shifting with the lowering sun. Only a few minutes remained before all sunlight would be gone from the trunk. Then a "whir-r-r" and the mydas fly was directly overhead. A quick sweep of the net, and this time there was no slip. This fly long remained the prize piece in the author's first collection, for he thought such an exciting fly must be something unknown.

ALTERING THE LANDSCAPE

It was only years later that he learned what this fly was, and that actually it was fairly common. Of late years, however, it seems to have become very rare. Nervous and erratic human beings, by continually redesigning the landscape to conform to short-sighted notions of land improvements, by cutting down trees, draining swamps, changing river courses, and building artificial dams (instead of letting the beavers do the dam-building), are destroying the earth's great heritage, not only of mydas flies, but of wild flowers, birds, animals, and beautiful scenery.

THE LARGEST MYDAS FLY

In the south-western United States, and in northern Mexico, one can see another showy mydas fly, the orange-winged *Mydas luteipennis*, which is larger than the eastern species. Do not confuse it with the "tarantula hawk", a spider-killing wasp that inhabits the same regions and resembles the fly.

The largest mydas fly known is *Mydas heros*, a Brazilian species. With its two-inch body and three-inch wing expanse it is truly a spectacular insect.

The family is best represented in the Americas, although Australia can claim nine species.

The larvae of the Mydas fly, like those of the Asilidae, live in decaying wood and vegetation.

THE BEE LOUSE—EXTRA CARGO FOR THE BEE

In this queer family (Braulidae), there is only one common species. This is the brownish, hairy, minute bee louse, *Braula coeca*. It is wingless, undoubtedly having lost its wings because it had no further use for them; for it is parasitic on bees. Bee lice are so small that scores of them may hitchhike from beehive to beehive to flower to beehive on the body of a single honeybee. Mostly, however, they stay in the hive, crawling about from bee to bee, taking food from the mouths of their hosts.

HAVOC IN A BEEHIVE

The larvae burrow through the comb, feeding on the honey or pollen, or the bee bread, as the mixture of the two is called. When numerous they can cause considerable damage to the comb.

The adults crawling about on the bees irritate them. So bothersome do these bugs become that a bee infested with them sets up a dance in the hive or on the alighting board. Round and round it turns, first in one direction and then in the other, trying vainly to rid itself of free riders.

The bee louse was first described in France in 1740, although it probably was known before this, and later was recognized as being widely distributed all over central Europe and along the Mediterranean. Man has transported it with his bees until it is now well established in most parts of the world where bee culture is practised.

SYRPHID FLIES, HOVER FLIES, OR FLOWER FLIES

The syrphids are colourful flies, usually yellow and banded or lined with black, or black spotted with yellow. When not resting in flowers, feeding on the pollen, the flies may be found in the air, about eight to twelve feet above the ground, hovering on rapidly vibrating wings. They remain in a stationary position for minutes at a time, then dart off, too quickly to be seen, to a new location.

For this hovering, the syrphids select a sunlit woodland path, or a bright country lane, lined with trees, or occasionally an open weedy meadow.

A dozen or more of one species will gather in a shaft of sunlight, to romp among themselves, chasing one another, hovering, then chasing again, seemingly on tireless wings.

LARVAE WITH CURIOUS HABITS

The larvae of the family Syrphidae are extremely variable in their habits.

Some live in the nests of termites or ants, and feed on the dry pellets ejected by their hosts. Others live in the nests of bees and wasps.

One group lives in the liquids produced by decaying vegetable material or filth. These are the Rat-tailed Maggots, which have an extended, tail-like tube used for breathing while the larvae are immersed, head down, in the liquid. This apparatus may be from one to three times the length of the larvae. A European species, *Myiatropa florea*, has a respiratory tube ten inches long, or at least twelve times as long as the maggot.

Another group feeds upon aphids and mealy bugs or soft scab (the crusty spots on diseased plants and trees). Still others bore into wood and into the wounds in trees, into bulbs, and into the foliage of plants.

One of the largest and most beautiful species in the eastern United States is *Milesia virginiensis*. It is alternately banded with yellow, black, and brown. This syrphid fly used to be common a number of years ago, but of late very few have been seen. It seems to enjoy resting in the sunshine on the trunks of dead trees.

The Drone Fly, *Eristalis tenax*, which has spread from its original home along the Mediterranean to the Western Hemisphere, is yellow and black and looks very much like the male honeybee, or drone bee. This resemblance, plus the fact that its larvae live and pupate in decaying flesh, fooled ancient Greek and Roman pastoral writers into believing that bees generated from the bodies of dead animals.

BOTFLIES AND WARBLE FLIES— COLOURFUL BUT TROUBLESOME

Many present-day insect experts have split up the Oestridae family into a number of separate families. For convenience in this book, and because the botflies in general have quite similar habits, we are retaining the older classification and grouping them all in one family.

All botflies are medium-to-large, hairy, husky insects, somewhat resembling bees. Their eyes are smaller than those of most flies. All of their larvae are parasitic on mammals, including man. Since they lead extremely interesting lives, let us consider a few of them separately.

The Horse Botfly or **Nit Fly,** *Gasterophilus equi*, might be mistaken for a large bee, except for its white face. Although slow of flight, it usually succeeds in rushing in and laying its pale-yellow eggs and fastening them singly to the hairs of the legs, chests, and shoulders of horses, mules, and donkeys. This, in spite of the fact that the animals are trying constantly to drive the flies away.

When the eggs are hatching, the tickling young larvae are licked from the victim's hair. From the animal's tongue they travel down its throat into its stomach. By means of hooks around their mouths they attach themselves to the stomach walls. In badly infested stomachs the walls are completely covered with the wriggling larvae which, when fully grown, are three-quarters of an inch long.

The larvae spend the winter feeding. In the spring they are fully grown. Then, releasing their hold on the victim's stomach, they pass out with the droppings. Burrowing into the soil they pupate, emerging as adults in the summer, ready to mate and lay eggs for the next generation.

The Nose Botfly, *Gasterophilus haemorrhoidalis*, a closely related species, lays its eggs on the lips of the horse. From here it passes into the stomach of the animal, and the rest of its life is much like that of the horse botfly.

The Cattle Warble, or **Heel Fly,** *Hypoderma lineata*, is a species which bothers cattle. These flies are large and heavy and are covered with black and white hairs, with extra tufts of white hair on each side of the thorax. The female fastens her small, white eggs to the hairs of her victim's forelegs and sides. Some of the newly hatched larvae are sure to be licked off the hairs and eventually to reach the animal's throat. From there they work their way through the connective tissues until they reach the back.

Just under the hide the larvae stop and begin to feed. As they grow they form a lump, or "warble", which can be felt or seen quite easily. If you examine it closely you will discover a small hole in the top of the lump, through which the larva breathes and discharges its waste material. When fully grown the larva leaves through this opening, drops to the ground, and burrows in to form a pupa.

In the author's youth, one of the farm boy's chores was to pop the bot out of the cow's back by pressing the sides of the lump with his fingers. These holes heal, but they leave a weak place in the hide, greatly reducing its value. Tanners refer to skins with such weak spots as "grubby" hides.

Several other closely related species attack various other mammals, from field mice to deer.

The Sheep Botfly or **Sheep Gadfly,** *Oestrus ovis*, is usually the cause when you see sheep stampeding around the pasture on a hot summer's day. It is a husky, hairy, yellowish insect about half an inch long, and a very fast flier. The female sometimes carries her eggs until they hatch. She lays her eggs or deposits her larvae in the nostrils of sheep or goats. In spite of its desperate attempts the animal is seldom able to evade this persistent and speedy fly.

The larvae spend their entire lives, from summer through the winter and into the next spring, in the nostrils and sinuses of their hosts. Their presence causes great pain and frequently death, for they measure over an inch in length, and if a number are present can constrict the passages. This disease is known as "staggers", or "grub-in-the-head", or "false gid".

When mature, the larvae drop to the ground, where they burrow in to pupate. In a few weeks the adult fly emerges, ready to start the next generation.

The sheep botfly originally made its home in the Old World, but it has travelled with its hosts until it is now cosmopolitan. Closely related species infest a number of animals, especially the deer group, but also kangaroos, elephants, rabbits, and man.

The Human Botfly, *Dermatobia hominis.* Most of the botflies live the simple, easy lives of ordinary parasites, but the one that lives on man leads a comparatively complicated and dangerous existence. Found only in the Western Hemisphere it is a large, hairy fly with large wings and, in contrast to many other botflies, it has large eyes.

The female of this fly lays its eggs on mosquitoes, other flies, or ticks; the eggs hatch on these animals. If one of these carriers comes in contact with man, the fly larvae transfer to man. Boring through the human skin they establish themselves in the muscle tissues, and feed there until they are fully grown, a matter of forty-five to fifty-five days. As you can imagine, this procedure is very painful to the victim.

If not successful in reaching their ultimate host, the botfly larvae soon die. This is the weak link in their life, and if it were not for this the fly would be more abundant and might become a serious pest.

——THE SPEED OF THE BOTFLY. One of the most frequent questions to come into the author's office concerns the reputed great speed of the botfly. Two hundred to seven hundred miles per hour are the usual figures appearing in fiction. Although botflies are rapid in flight, particularly the deer botfly, the actual speed of their flight probably does not exceed fifty miles, and probably reaches this figure only for short, darting flights. A more conservative estimate, and one probably nearer the truth, claims their flight to be about thirty to forty miles an hour.

TACHINA FLIES—OUR FRIENDLY SERVANTS

The author's introduction to the tachina flies (family Tachinidae) came years ago. He had collected a number of the spring caterpillars of the Camberwell Beauty butterfly, which he kept in a screened box, carefully fed, and watched as they all selected spots and hung themselves up by the two legs at the tips of their abdomens. There they remained suspended, each from its little pad of silk, arching, head down in a J-shaped position.

The expected next stage in their transformation never occurred. There was no sign that the skin would split down the back, as described in books, to reveal the pupa. Instead, these caterpillars were gradually shrivelling. And then it became apparent that a number of insects which at first appeared to be houseflies were in the cage. How did they get in?

Next, the author discovered they were not houseflies, and something he had read earlier came to mind; that these were tachina flies. The parent of these flies had laid her eggs on the caterpillars before the latter were collected. Hatching, the grubs had fed inside, four or five to each living caterpillar.

Tachina flies are a bane to all lepidopterists trying to rear butterflies and moths from field-collected larvae, but they are a blessing to the rest of humanity, for they destroy a great many of the insects that we consider pests. Not only do tachina flies attack many of the moths that feed on our food, but various species also feed on beetles, earwigs, grasshoppers, bugs, wasps, or other flies.

TACHINA FLIES IN ACTION

More than five thousand species of tachinas have been described, 1,500 of them having been seen in North America; many new ones are constantly being added. Among these thousands, their detailed habits are quite variable. A lifetime could be spent working out the life histories of just a few of them. As far as we know, however, all of the species prey upon other insects.

The tachina flies lay their eggs on, or in, the victim; or, sometimes, they deposit them on foliage, where they may be swallowed by their host, or where the hatched larvae may lie in wait to attach themselves to their prey. Fifty to as many as five thousand eggs may be deposited by the adult fly, depending upon the various species. Those that deposit the larger number of eggs are the species that drop them on grass and foliage where, of course, the mortality to egg and larva is very high. Some species carry the eggs until they are hatched on the parent.

Once inside their host the grubs live a life of ease until they are fully developed. Then they pupate, either in the remains of the victim or on the ground. The adults range in size from one-sixteenth of an inch to a full inch. Most of them are fierce-looking creatures, covered as they are with an armour of bristles.

Bombyliomyia abrupta is one of the attractive species in the eastern United States. It has a large, reddish-yellow abdomen, greenish-yellow thorax, and clear wings veined in yellow. Its body is covered with scattered, stiff black bristles. You will find it along pathways on the edges of woods, basking in the sunshine, or scouting for a future host for its children.

It is impossible to list the numerous species in this family, but to the student wishing to specialize in a limited group, these flies are recommended as an intriguing and rewarding family to study. A collection neatly arranged offers a beautiful display to show to your friends.

BLOWFLIES, SCAVENGER FLIES, AND FLESH FLIES

Although all the members of this large family (Sarcophagidae) have disgusting habits, one group does the world an immense amount of good, for they are scavengers. They are quick to lay their eggs on dead animal matter. The larvae, equally quickly, reduce it from an obnoxious condition to one unnoticeable and readily blended with the soil. Some species apply the same clean-up methods to decaying vegetable material.

Dangerous to Man. Unfortunately, most of the blowflies are parasitic and dangerous to man and beast. Many of them place their larvae in the wounds of animals or man. Some of these cause infections of the eyes, ears, nose, and head. Even some of these parasitic species may be considered beneficial to man, however, because they destroy snails and grasshoppers. Others are parasitic on beetles, spiders, bees, and wasps.

In all there are about a thousand known species, ranging in size from very small to more than half an inch. Their grey-mottled abdomens bristling with scattered hairs, their striped thoraxes, and especially their reddish eyes will help you to recognize the members of this family.

ROOT MAGGOT FLIES—ENEMIES OF CROPS

An important family to the gardener is Anthomyiidae, for it contains a great many species that destroy his crops.

The Cabbage Maggot, *Phorbia brassicae*, produces larvae that are highly injurious to crops. They attack the stems and roots of young plants just set out, causing them to wilt and die. They also attack radishes, cauliflower, and others of the cabbage family. Old stalks or dead plants left in the garden harbour the insects over the winter and these should therefore be burned during the winter.

Phorbia fusciceps, introduced into the United States from Europe before 1856, is more general in its feeding habits. It not only attacks the cabbage family, but corn, onions, and other garden plants. *Phorbia cepetorum*, also introduced, and its native cousin, *ceparum*, do considerable damage to onions. Another, *rubivora*, girdles the tips of raspberry and blackberry shoots. Others, such as *Pegomyia vicina*, mine the leaves of beets and spinach, making blotchy leaves, unsuitable for market.

The Lesser Housefly, *Fannia canicularis*, together with some others of the same genus, is an immigrant from Europe. It breeds in dung and decaying material, making itself troublesome about houses in regions that do not possess proper sanitary facilities.

THE HOUSEFLY—AN AGE-OLD PEST

The Common Housefly, *Musca domestica*, is of course the most familiar representative of its family (Muscidae). It was probably associated with man long before he had acquired and domesticated animals. Undoubtedly, it has been one of the most serious pests with which he has had to contend.

This creature neither bites nor stings, but it contaminates our food by its insanitary habit of walking over unclean material and then, perhaps the next moment, visiting the kitchen or dining room. It has been known to carry and transmit many diseases, the most common of which are typhoid fever, bacillary and amoebic dysentery, trachoma, cholera, and even tuberculosis.

MODERN METHODS KEEP THE HOUSEFLY IN CHECK. The author can remember the days when flies by the hundreds, yes, thousands, would congregate about every farmyard, house, or apartment. Screening had little effect, because usually it was inadequately done. Now, however, with the automobile, and its resulting elimination of the old-style horse and cow stables, and the prevalence of sewerage systems, the fly has practically disappeared from many places. This is particularly true in the large urban areas.

Today, with adequate screens to prevent most flies and mosquitoes from entering, and with DDT sprayed in strategic spots in a house to get the few stragglers that do make their way in, we need not worry about a fly invasion.

The female housefly lays five hundred to two thousand eggs, which may hatch in a few days. The larval period is less than five days, and the pupation stage about an equal time. Therefore, the entire life cycle, under favourable temperature and climatic conditions, can be as short as eleven or twelve days. Lower temperatures may extend the cycle to a month or more.

The family Muscidae at one time was one of the largest of the fly families. Recently, entomologists have been pruning it down by raising entire sections of it to family rank. For our purpose, we will consider these flies more or less as a whole group. In general, they all have pretty nearly the same habits, being primarily scavengers.

The Stable Fly, *Stomoxys calcitrans.* On those muggy days or evenings when the heavens seem all set to release the rain, everyone has noticed that the houseflies have gone crazy and turned biters. Vainly we drive them away, only to have them return with renewed vigour to the attack. Ankles, neck and hands seem to be the selected spots.

Looking at the pests more carefully, we see at once that they are not houseflies. They are shorter, with a more rounded abdomen, and differ decidedly in having a long, piercing mouth-part instead of the broad, rasping process of the familiar housefly. These are the stable flies.

Both sexes are bloodsuckers. Because they seem to be more vicious before, or during, summer rains, these flies have also acquired the name of storm fly. Domestic and wild animals suffer tremendously from these insects.

The Horn Fly, *Haematobia irritans,* is so called from its habit of sucking blood at the base of the horns of cattle. It is also called the Texas fly, because it was believed to have invaded the East from that state. Actually, the fly came from Europe and was first noticed about 1887. Of late years, it has become rather rare in the United States.

The Cluster Fly, *Pollenia rudis,* a fly that looks very much like a housefly, is frequently seen walking slowly about in the house. It received its popular name from its habit of collecting in numbers. It will gather, particularly in the autumn, in groups of eight or ten, behind a picture, books, or among boxes. When disturbed, it does not attempt to fly but walks slowly away. The wings are carried overlapped, giving the fly an appearance of length.

The life history of the cluster fly is especially interesting because it is believed that its larvae feed upon earthworms, which in turn are living in manure or decaying vegetation.

The Screwworm, *Chrysomyia macellaria,* produces larvae which can be dangerous creatures. Normally, they feed on carrion, but occasionally they attack living animals. The eggs are laid in open wounds, or in the nose of an animal. If laid in the nose, the larvae may reach the head cavities, a condition sometimes resulting in death to the animal or man.

This fly is bluish in colour and is frequently confused with the so-called "bluebottle flies" described below.

Blowflies or **Bluebottle Flies.** The genus *Calliphora* contains several flies known as blowflies, also as bluebottle flies. These flies hatch within twenty-four hours. Sometimes they have already hatched in the mother's body, in which case she deposits the living larvae. The larval and pupal stages each require from ten to twelve days, the pupal usually the longer. *Calliphora vomitoria* is the most common in the United States.

Lucilia has three common species of bluebottle flies: *sylvarum* is bright blue; *caesar* is greenish; and *sericata* has a bronze tint. Carrion is the principal food of all three, although they do breed in all types of offensive material.

THE DEADLY TSETSE FLY

Although the tsetse flies are found only in Africa, no book on insects could omit this family (Glossinidae), which is so deadly to man, his animals, and the wild animals of large areas in central Africa.

The tsetse flies are not outstanding in appearance, considering the reputation they have acquired. In fact, they might be mistaken for oversized houseflies, differing, to the layman's eyes, in being more brownish. It is with a feeling of disappointment that a museum visitor gazes for the first time at the innocuous-looking specimen labelled "tsetse fly".

The eggs develop singly. A larva is carried in the body of the mother and is fed by special glands. When mature, it is placed on the ground in a shady spot close to a stream or wet place. Burrowing in, the larva pupates; the adult emerges in about thirty days. Both sexes are blood-suckers. Many of them carry the trypanosomes that are the cause of African sleeping sickness, a disease that is usually fatal to man and animals alike.

A Small But Dangerous Family. The family is a very small one, with only twenty-one species (all belonging to the genus *Glossina*). The species fall into three groups, each taking the name of the principal species of that group.

The *fusca* group, named after *Glossina fusca*, contains ten species. All of these play little part in the transmission of African sleeping sickness.

The *palpalis* group, named after *Glossina palpalis*, contains five species. The members of this group are instrumental in transmitting *Trypanosoma gambiense* to man, resulting in the Gambian sleeping sickness; *uniforme* to sheep and goats; and *vivax* to cattle and horses, causing the disease called souma.

The *morsitans* group, from *Glossina morsitans*, contains six species.

These flies transmit to man *Trypanosoma rhodesiense*, the cause of Rhodesian sleeping sickness; to cattle and horses, *brucei*, the cause of nagana, a fatal disease; to cattle and wild grazers, *caprae*, causing souma in cattle; to swine, *suis*, causing a similar disease.

PEACOCK FLIES

This small family (Trypetidae) is interesting only because of the adult flies, which strut about waving their wings back and forth in a very rhythmical manner. Although rather small, usually less than a quarter of an inch, many peacock flies are quite attractively marked. Their wings are marked with a variety of dark spots or bands, a feature which adds to their beauty as they gently fan the wings to and fro.

FLAT FLIES—HARDLY FLIES AT ALL

This family (Hippoboscidae) and two other small families are grouped here at the end of the flies, because those who specialize in the study of Diptera regard them as a distinct sub-order. As the result of their long parasitic life on the coverings of animals, they have become so changed in structure and habits as to make them seem not to be Diptera.

Numbering about four hundred species, the Hippoboscidae are parasitic upon birds and mammals, sometimes killing their hosts. They live in the feathers or fur, sucking the hosts' blood.

Most of them are flattened and are thus able to slip through the animals' covering.

The genus *Olfersia* contains winged species which are usually found on hawks and owls. If one host dies or is killed, the flies leave the body, flying off in search of another host. At this time, they may settle on almost any bird or animal that is near.

A PERSISTENT PEST

The author has had some of these flies settle on him. One in particular was determined to seek shelter on the author, and he was equally determined to capture it for a specimen. It would get under the collar or lapels of his coat, under his hat, or in his hair or clothing. Each time it would settle, he would try to grab it, only to have it slip through his

Several species of polistes wasps are common in the United States. As is the case with many social wasps the young queen after hibernating through the winter starts a colony in the spring. She builds a few cells of the comb, lays an egg in each and, like the carpenter ant, tends this small-scale operation until she raises a brood of workers. Wasps, bees and ants belong to the order Hymenoptera. The name is generally interpreted "membrane wings", but some naturalists believe it refers to the fact that the insects mate in flight. Hymenoptera have two pairs of wings, but the front edge of the smaller second pair is normally closely secured to the rear edge of the first pair by a series of minute hooks, giving the appearance of a single pair. *See page 2006*

[16-7]

[16-7A]

Bees differ from wasps in a number of minor ways, one of the more apparent of which is the densely haired body of most bee species. Many bumblebees measure an inch or more in length, but some species are less than three-eighths of an inch long. As with the wasps, the colony is started each spring by a young queen which has hibernated through the winter. The nest is constructed in a hole in the ground and may be ten or twelve inches wide by autumn. Bumblebees have longer tongues than honeybees and are very useful in pollinizing blossoms with long corolla such as alfalfa and the clovers. *See page 2006*

The legs of the honeybee are equipped for pollen gathering. One joint of the forelegs has a brush of stiff hairs for cleaning the hairy compound eyes. At its lower end this joint has a flat movable spine which closes over a bristle-lined notch in the adjacent joint, forming an antenna cleaner. Longer hairs on the lower end form a brush to gather pollen from the fore parts of the body. The middle legs have brushes for removing pollen from the forelegs, and each bears a spur for picking up wax. The wide tibia of the hind leg is slightly concave and has a margin of incurving hairs, forming the pollen basket. On the inner surface of the lower joint is the pollen comb—about 10 rows of stiff, downward-pointing spines. Pollen is passed from the front to the middle legs which are then drawn through the combs. Each hind leg is scraped over the opposite leg and the pollen is packed into the baskets by flexing the joints.

See page 2007

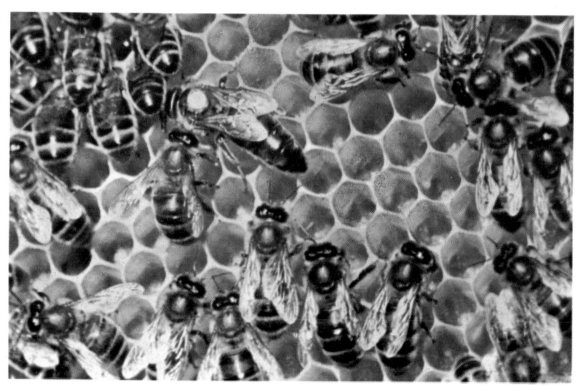

[16-8A]

When a honeybee returns to the hive other worker bees unload its bulging pollen baskets. Still others take charge of the nectar which the homecoming bee discharges from its large crop or honey stomach. The wax for the honeycombs is secreted as small flakes by glands in pockets under the abdomen on workers. The bees work and mould the wax with their smooth mandibles and once a comb is formed it may be used for years. Bees are active all year; during the winter they feed on stored honey, and keep the hive warm by clustering. In the summer they "air condition" the hive by fanning their wings vigorously. Workers hatched in the autumn may survive until spring, but those hatched earlier live only about six or eight weeks. Queens live from three to five years and although they may lay a million eggs, they mate only once.

See page 2007

A BIG-GAME HUNTER OF THE INSECT WORLD, AND ITS PREY

The robber fly, which feeds on other insects, is so audacious that it thinks nothing of seizing a
victim much heavier than itself. With its two front legs it clings desperately to the twig while
it grasps the prey, a dragonfly, with its middle and hind legs. It will not drop the dragonfly.
See page 1967.

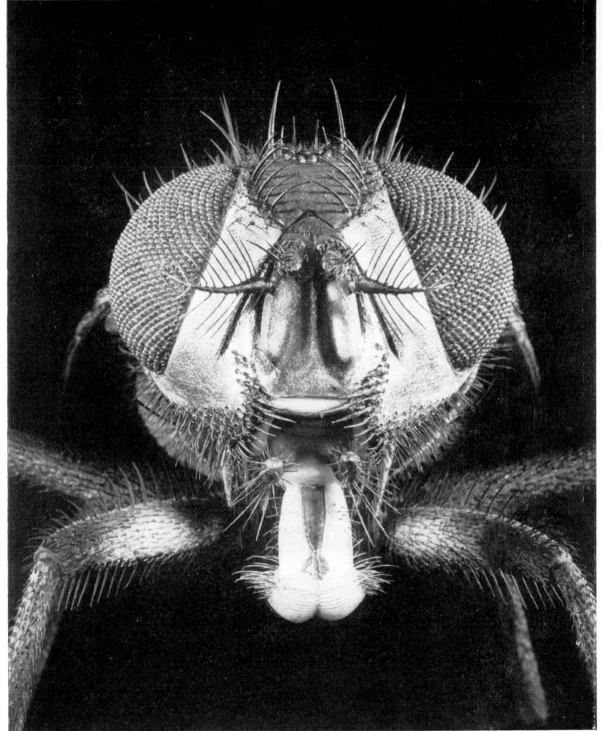

MAGNIFIED FACE OF THE COMMON HOUSEFLY

It looks like a marvellously engraved and jewelled brooch; the design is intricate and the craft-manship perfect. Those huge, beaded mounds at the left and right are the compound eyes of the insects. They are set with thousands of tiny lenses, giving the fly remarkably good vision. The object at the bottom is the tongue. It is fitted, at the tip, with a rasp or grater. This scrapes the food into small portions, serving the housefly the way teeth do the higher animals. *See page 1978.*

fingers and fly away. It would then seem to leave the scene, but no, back it would come, and duck into some crevice.

Time after time the fly would escape the author's searching fingers. The chase lasted for fifteen minutes or more until success was finally achieved.

A FLAT FLY WITHOUT WINGS

If you wish to see a wingless member of this family, any flock of sheep will yield examples. This is *Melophagus ovinus*, commonly called the "sheep tick". Superficially, it does look like a tick, but can at once be recognized by the presence of only three pairs of legs. The adults are dark brown, with a long proboscis. They measure about a fifth of an inch long. Wherever sheep have been taken, this pest has travelled along. It irritates the sheep with its blood sucking, and if enough of these insects are gathered they kill the animal. They also stain and soil the wool, thus reducing its value.

BAT TICKS

With few exceptions, the members of the two families making up this group (Nycteribiidae and Streblidae) have no wings, although the halteres (the little knoblike organs) are present and well developed. Almost all of them live on bats, and that is how they come by their name.

The Fleas, Including the Jiggers

EVERYONE HAS HEARD about fleas. Many a person has met them, either on himself or on his pets. Yet we can hardly say that we know what they look like; all we see is a bouncing speck.

Under a microscope, however, a flea shows up as a most interestingly constructed insect. It is compact, wingless, usually reddish brown, with short forelegs and middle legs and very long hind legs, and the whole body is sparsely covered with short, stiff hairs all pointing backwards.

Its flat sides enable the flea to slide easily through the hairs of its host. Its backward-pointing spines or hairs also assist its forward progress and hamper the host's efforts to scratch it out. The remarkable thing about fleas is their ability to jump. Like the leaf hoppers, grasshoppers, and other hoppers of the insect world, fleas can jump many times their own length. If man were endowed with proportionate skill, he could easily leap one hundred yards.

As we know only too well, adult fleas are bloodsuckers. The different species tend to feed upon different birds or mammals. Although they prefer a particular species of host, many are not averse to trying another if their favoured brand of food is not conveniently near. On the other hand, they can live without food for a long time.

Contrary to the common notion, the larvae are not bloodsuckers, but feed upon the scales of skin and debris of plant or animal matter that collects in homes, stores, or factories. Even the dust in the floor cracks contains enough nourishment to feed many hundreds of flea grubs. These are small, white, wormlike creatures, under an eighth of an inch in length. When grown, the larva pupates in a round, flat, thin, silken cocoon. The eggs are white and barely visible on a black cloth. They are dropped at random by the female, wherever she may happen to be at the time. (Fleas make up the order Siphonaptera.)

COMMON PESTS

The Dog Flea, *Ctenocephalus canis*, is the most common of our household fleas. It is not partial to dogs alone, but is equally at home on cats, rabbits, and rats, and is not at all reluctant to try man as a dwelling place.

Just about as abundant, the Cat Flea, *Ctenocephalus felis*, also feeds on cats, dogs, rats, and man.

The Human Flea, *Pulex irritans*, is common in parts of Europe and the rest of the Eastern Hemisphere but quite scarce in North America. It has never seemed able to adjust itself to American conditions of living. Also chiefly confined to the Eastern Hemisphere are some eleven species of fleas that transmit bubonic plague from rats to man.

Jiggers—Different Feeding Habits. One family of fleas has feeding habits rather different from those of the fleas we have been considering. The chigoe, or jigger, *Dermatophilus penetrans*, originally from South America, is a typical species. The male feeds externally, but the female burrows into the flesh around the feet of domestic animals, birds, and man. There it lives and deposits its eggs. It digs in under the toenails of the barefoot natives of the tropical countries, causing bad sores. This jigger is not to be confused with the mite of the southern United States, which is also called a jigger.

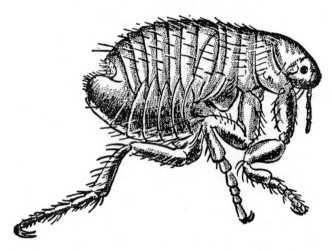

THE FLEA—FUSSY ABOUT ITS FOOD

Each kind of flea prefers the blood of one kind of animal or bird; there are dog fleas, cat fleas, rat fleas, and so on. If they are very hungry, animal fleas can and will attack persons. The flea shown above (greatly enlarged) has a special taste for human beings; it is an Eastern Hemisphere flea and has never been very successful in North America.

The Tropical Hen Flea, *Echidnophaga gallinacea,* is another flea that is parasitical on birds. It is also called the "sticktight flea" because it clings so closely to its host. It is a serious pest on poultry as well as on wild birds in many parts of the world. Hundreds of these fleas are sometimes seen adhering to the bare spots around the bill, eyes, comb, and wattles of domestic fowl.

Ants, Bees, Wasps, and Their Relatives

THE ANTS, bees, wasps, and their kind, order Hymenoptera ("membrane wings"), are often confused with the Diptera, or true flies. Each order wears thin, membranous wings with supporting veins. The Hymenoptera, however, have two pairs of wings, while the Diptera have but one pair.

Very often you will have to observe a hymenopterous insect carefully before you can be sure that it does have four wings. That is because the second pair of wings is usually much smaller than the first pair. And, still more confusing, the second pair is normally closely hooked to the first pair by a series of minute hooks, called hamuli, along the front margin, which engage with a fold on the rear edge of the forewings. This interesting structure for fastening the two wings together is visible only with the aid of a good lens, or under a microscope.

The commonest groups of the Hymenoptera, that is, the bees, the wasps (or hornets), and the ants, are very well known to most people for other distinctive characteristics, not the least of which are the very efficient stingers with which most of them are equipped. Some bees and many ants have no stingers, but ants frequently have a good pair of jaws, which they know only too well how to use.

Some Hymenoptera carry a most dangerous-looking weapon, apparently an enormous stinger, sometimes three or four inches long. This instrument is not a stinger but a combination drill and ovipositor, which its owner, a female ichneumon fly, will use to deposit her eggs under the bark of trees.

A GREAT GROUP—125,000 SPECIES

The Hymenoptera, with its 125,000 described species, is now the second-largest order of insects. It is exceeded only by the Coleoptera

1986

(beetles), which has 300,000 known species. It has been estimated, moreover, that another 125,000 Hymenoptera, mostly very small insects, have yet to be described. Like most other groups of insects, they reach their highest development and numbers in tropical countries. About seven thousand species inhabit North America.

Since the Hymenoptera are divided into several groups called super-families, each superfamily composed of groups with fairly similar characteristics, it is the superfamilies that we shall discuss, instead of families, except when the latter are unusually distinctive or important.

SAWFLIES—THE FEMALE CARRIES A SAW

The sawflies differ from all other Hymenoptera in that they have no marked constriction at the base of the abdomen where it joins with the thorax. In other words, the sawflies are not "wasp-waisted". The females may also be recognized by their "saws", two flattened, pointed, usually yellowish plates sliding between two other external plates, the "saw guides", on the under-side, at the tip of the abdomen.

This whole structure makes up the ovipositor, or egg-depositing apparatus. Some sawfly species have much larger ovipositors than others. With her ovipositor, the sawfly cuts an opening in the particular plant tissue she prefers for her young, and then inserts an egg. The place selected, depending upon the species, may be leaves, stems, tree trunks, or their branches. Some sawflies develop galls (enlarged plant growths) on leaves or stems, in which their larvae live and feed.

The larvae of all sawflies are plant feeders, and many of them look like the caterpillars of butterflies and moths. They can usually be distinguished from caterpillars by the absence of abdominal legs; if these are present, they do not have the circles of hooks that we see on the abdominal legs of caterpillars. A sure difference, however, is the presence of only one simple eye (ocellus) on each side of the head of the sawfly larva, whereas a caterpillar has several. Sawflies are classed as a superfamily, Tenthredinoidea.

The Elm Sawfly, *Cimbex americana,* is one of the common and larger species in the United States. The author would be inclined to call it the willow sawfly, for in his experience the larva is more commonly found feeding upon willow leaves than upon elm. But since elms ˰ ˯ considered more valuable than willows, insect experts have taken this factor into consideration in applying a common name. The elm sawfly also feeds upon poplar and lime trees, and perhaps occasionally on other trees.

The fleshy, greenish-white larva of this insect always clings with the end of its body encircling a stem or twig. When ready to pupate, it spins a rough cocoon among old leaves. The large, shining adult is steel blue-black, dotted with several white spots on the side of its abdomen, and has smoke-coloured wings two inches across.

The Pigeon Tremex, *Tremex columba,* is one of a group of sawflies commonly called "horntails", because of the short, thick spine, or horn, at the end of the male bodies.

The pigeon tremex is a large, blundering insect nearly two inches long. It has a large head on a very slender neck. Its glistening, purplish-red abdomen is banded with yellow. Its many-veined, smoky wings may spread as much as two and a half inches The female has a con-spicuous ovipositor through which she inserts her eggs into the trunks of maple, elm, or other forest trees.

You will never see the horntail's larvae unless you have the time and energy to dig them out of the trees, for they bore into the wood, sometimes as much as several inches.

CHALCID FLIES—INCLUDING THE SMALLEST OF INSECTS

To mankind, the chalcid flies (superfamily Chalcidoidea) are just about the most important of all the insects. Not even the bees are more useful to us. For the chalcid flies are parasites that kill a great many of the insects that compete with us for our food supplies. They deposit their eggs in a great many plant-eating insects and insect larvae, from tomato worms and cabbage worms down to aphids and scale insects. They also parasitize ticks and spiders.

Not all chalcid flies are parasitic; a few are seed eaters. One of these, the famous *Blastophaga psense*, pollinates the Smyrna fig.

Looking at some of the chalcids, you will find it hard to believe that they wield so much power in the world of insects. The largest of them is scarcely an eighth of an inch long, and most are much smaller. There are chalcid flies that spend all their lives in the body of an aphid or a scale. What is supposed to be the smallest of all insects is the chalcid *Alaptus magnanimus*, eight one-thousandths of an inch long. It is a parasite on book lice.

CYNIPID FLIES—THEY PREY ON WEEDS

A big group of very small insects, the cynipid flies (superfamily Cynipoidea) are largely gall makers, especially on oak trees, although some breed in the galls formed by others, taking no part in the formation. Others are parasitic on a variety of insects.

In general, these flies are beneficial to man, even some of those that are gall makers; for they attack plants that in the human classification are called weeds, such as goldenrod and sunflowers.

THE "MAY BEETLE PARASITE" AND ITS KIN

Almost all of the insects in the next group, superfamily Serphoidea, are parasitic. Most of them are very small, for many of them pass their entire life cycle in an egg of another insect. For this reason, few are ever seen except by a specialist studying these small insects. There are still hundreds as yet unrecognized.

An Insect That Lives on May Beetle Grubs. One rather large species fascinating to observe is *Pelecinus polyturator*. Although it has never been given a common name, it might well be called the "May Beetle Parasite", for this curious insect lives on May Beetle grubs. The female, who always seems to know where to find her prey, inserts her two-inch-long, very slender abdomen into the ground and lays an egg upon the grub. She is shining black, with a wing-spread of only one inch. You wonder how those small, transparent wings can transport this largish insect.

The male is entirely different, and for a long time was not known. It has the same black colour and the same transparent wings. Instead of the long, slender body, however, it has a roundish abdomen, the first two segments of which are short and slender, giving the insect a wasplike look. Only a few specimens of the male exist in the large insect collections of the United States. It is, therefore, believed to be quite rare. Perhaps we do not know just where to look for it.

ICHNEUMON FLIES—HELPFUL OR HARMFUL?

Man owes a great deal to this large group of ichneumon "wasps". They work indirectly for us day after day by destroying other insects. Not that they are intentionally beneficial to mankind. They simply like to eat the insects that like to eat our food plants. Actually, the ichneumon flies destroy just as many useful insects as harmful ones; but they serve an extremely important function in preserving what we call the "balance of nature".

The group (superfamily Ichneumonoidea) is so large and complex, with the species in many cases so closely resembling one another, that it is possible to give only a general idea of a few of the species. Perhaps the largest and most conspicuous species should be mentioned first.

SOME OF THE LARGE ICHNEUMONS

A number of these belong to the genus *Megarhyssa*, sometimes called *Thalessa*. You can recognize the female at once by the very long ovipositor, which varies, according to the species, from two to four, or

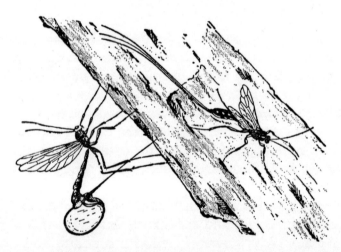

LONG-TAILED ICHNEUMON FLIES PROTECT OUR FORESTS
The female of these curious creatures has a tube two to five inches long which she can bore into a tree trunk until it reaches the tunnel of some wood-eating insect. Through the tube she deposits her eggs, which, when hatched, will eat the other insects.

five, inches in length. They are parasitic upon wood-boring larvae of the sawflies, and particularly the genus *Tremex*. With the long, slender ovipositor, the female is able to penetrate solid wood to a depth of several inches and deposit an egg in the burrow of the *Tremex* larva.

Extraordinary Ways of the Female. Another remarkable thing about the female is her ability to locate the exact spot where she should bore. Perhaps she can hear the sound the feeding *Tremex* larva makes.

In a forest in the summer the female exploring a tree trunk can easily be observed. Carefully she examines a certain area, tapping gently with her antennae. Back and forth she moves, as she examines. Apparently satisfied, she firmly fastens the claws of her feet in the bark, then, rearing her abdomen upward on her widely stretched legs, she places the tip of her ovipositor directly below the tip of her abdomen, with the drill guides, one on each side, forming a tube through which the ovipositor can work.

AN INGENIOUS ADAPTATION

The insect is unable, however, to elevate her abdomen to hold the entire ovipositor vertical. She has therefore developed an ingenious adaptation of her abdomen and is able to retract the base of her ovipositor within the last two abdominal segments, which are quite membranous. More and more they stretch, as the ovipositor is curved within them, until they resemble a thin, transparent, flattened balloon.

At about the time you expect the balloon to burst, the insect has the ovipositor in position and ready to drill. Slowly but steadily it starts to pierce the wood, for at the tip are tiny teeth that saw the fibre apart.

——A DANGEROUS OPERATION. Woe betide the ichneumon if anything disturbs her at her drilling, for she may not be able to withdraw the ovipositor, in which case it is torn away as the insect seeks to escape. Even in the ordinary course of events, she is sometimes unable to extract her ovipositor because of swelling of the wood, and she either dies or breaks loose, leaving her ovipositor in the tree.

Megarhyssa atrata is the largest species in this genus. It is black, with smoky wings. A few fine, yellow lines mark the thorax and the tip of the abdomen.

Megarhyssa lunatar is nearly as large as *atrata*. Its ovipositor is twice the length of its body. The body is very prettily marked with lateral stripes of yellow, brown, and a greyish shade.

A Careful Feeder. *Ophion macrurum* is a large ichneumon fly, reddish in colour, and possessing a very short ovipositor scarcely a quarter of an inch long. The lepidopterist rearing saturniid moths is certain sooner or later to have some of these parasitic wasps emerge from his cherished cocoons. The *Ophion* larva feeds within the caterpillar, careful not to kill it until the cocoon is finished. The *Ophion* then pushes the dead caterpillar aside and spins its own cocoon, a rough affair, inside the original.

A FAMILIAR ICHNEUMON

Familiar signs of an ichneumon parasite that many Americans have seen are the tiny, white, silken cocoons of one of the Braconidae carried around on the backs of sphingid caterpillars, especially on the tomato worm. Sometimes a gardener imagines that these cocoons are the eggs of the tomato worm, and carefully destroys them, thus killing insects that could do much more damage to tomato worms than he.

THE BUSY, BUSY ANTS

The word ant at once brings to mind the familiar wingless insect that gets into our picnic lunches or into our houses. Ants of this type are the workers of the various species, foraging for what they may find to eat or to carry home to feed the rest of the colony. Few persons realize that in each ant nest there are three classes of society, or castes. The castes may have several forms.

QUEENS, WORKERS, AND SOLDIERS

Outstanding in any typical colony is the queen; she is not a ruler in any sense of the word, but is the mother, and frequently the founder, of the colony. She lays the eggs from which all the other ants develop.

Most of these eggs produce individuals known as workers. These workers are imperfectly developed females, and their duties are innumerable. They forage and bring home the supplies to feed the queen and the other members of the family. They care for the eggs and the young. They enlarge the nest, clean it, and, if necessary, defend it.

This last duty is, however, frequently shared with the soldier caste, in those colonies that possess soldiers. The warrior caste usually differs from the workers in having larger heads with formidable jaws. There may even be several forms of these soldiers, differing in the size of the head and jaws.

THE MARRIAGE FLIGHT AND AFTERWARDS

In nearly every nest at some time in the year there are winged individuals.

These are, however, generally of two sizes. The smaller are the males, the larger the perfect females. For some unexplainable reason, on a certain day, generally towards evening, all of the colonies of a certain species for miles around will drive out the winged individuals. These will then try out their wings, for the first time, in a tremendous swarm, or marriage flight.

After mating, all drop to the ground. The males, which far out-number the females, quickly die or are eaten by birds or mammals. The females, after mating, tear off their wings and crawl under cover, and eventually seek a place in which they can attempt to establish a new colony.

Constructing a small chamber, a female will lay a few eggs, which she herself will tend, and will feed the young until a small nucleus of workers has developed. These workers then take over the active duties of the nest. From this time on the queen is simply an egg-laying machine.

HOW TO KEEP AN ANT NEST

You can keep a small colony of ants where you can watch them. They make intriguing pets. The simplest form of nest may be a tumbler, containing soil, and set in a pan of water. Into the tumbler, a small colony of ants (it must have a queen to be successful) is dumped. They will quickly build a nest to suit themselves. While this is the easiest arrangement, it is not the best, as only a small portion of the actual nest can be seen.

Two Kinds of Ant Nests. Two types of ant nests have been con-structed by man in order to raise and study ant life. The Janet Ant Nest is of cast plaster with two or more shallow chambers with narrow connecting passageways moulded in the plaster. These chambers are covered with glass and also an opaque cover to provide darkness. One or more chambers serve for the nest, and one is for food. The food chamber is not darkened.

The Fielde Ant Nest is constructed on the same principle, but has a sheet of glass for the bottom. On this are cemented strips of glass for walls, forming chambers which are connected by passageways.

Cemented on top of the glass strips are strips of coarse towelling; smaller sheets of glass, one to each chamber, rest on the towelling, which makes an effective barrier. Each chamber has an extra opaque cover or a sheet of amber-coloured glass to exclude light.

MANY KINDS OF ANTS

Although there are many species of ants, they are all quite similar in body formation. The ants are classed as a superfamily (Formicoidae), one family, the Formicidae, making up the entire superfamily.

Insects Mistaken for Ants. A number of insects are confused with ants. The Isoptera, or termites, sometimes called "white ants", are among these. Termites have habits and a social organization similar to those of ants, but are not at all like ants physically. It is remarkable that two such separate groups as ants and termites should have evolved along such parallel lines as are exhibited by their colonizing or social habits. Some flies, bees, and particularly the "Velvet Ants" (actually wasps) are also frequently mistaken for ants.

A true ant can be quickly recognized by the one or two roundish enlargements it has in the contracted part of the abdomen. The first enlargement or segment is called a petiole. If there is a second segment, this is called the postpetiole.

The Black Carpenter Ant, *Camponotus herculeanus pennsylvanicus*, is seldom noticed unless it has invaded homes, where it makes a nuisance of itself by getting into food or calmly wandering about on the floors and crawling on the kitchen sink. These insects are black, as their name indicates. The workers are three-eighths of an inch long, while the queens measure nearly one inch in length. The males are somewhat shorter.

DAMAGE TO TIMBERS AND GROWING TREES

If the only nuisance they committed were to wander through houses and get into food, we might put up with them, but carpenter ants like to establish their colonies in the timbers of houses. They chew out the wood fibre, forming chambers in which they live and raise their young. An extensive colony may so weaken part of the structure as to cause it to collapse. Carpenter ants frequently take over where termites have died out.

Black carpenter ants also frequently establish a colony in the heart of a tree. To eradicate them without killing the tree is extremely difficult, but can be accomplished by feeding them a poison mash. This is made by adding Paris green or arsenate of lead to a mixture of bran and molasses, with only enough water to make a thick paste. This poison mixture is so placed that the ants will find it and so that the other creatures cannot get at it. The ants finding it will carry enough of it home to feed the queen and poison the entire colony.

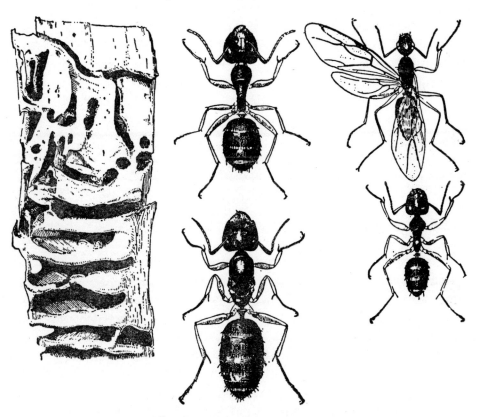

CARPENTER ANTS ARE ALMOST AS DESTRUCTIVE AS TERMITES

Usually the big black carpenter ants tunnel their homes in old logs and stumps; but as forests have been disappearing, the ants have moved into houses, weakening the timbers and raiding the kitchens for food. Shown in cross-section are carpenter ant tunnels, also four of the different castes. (*Top left*) Soldier or large worker. (*Top right*) Winged male. (*Bottom left*) Queen after she has torn off her wings. (*Bottom right*) Small worker.

The Herculean Ant of Europe, *Camponotus herculeanus*, is the largest species of this type in Europe. Other subspecies and varieties are found in other parts of the world.

The Black Honey Ant, *Camponotus inflatus*, is a closely related species. Ants of this type store honey for use during less bountiful times, and have a unique way of doing this. Volunteer workers, called repletes, engorge themselves until their abdomens are greatly distended. They remain like this until relieved of their loads by the other ants when food is not so plentiful.

In the south-western United States and extending down into Central and South America, species of the genus *Myrmecocystus* also use repletes to store honey. These repletes cling to the ceilings of their underground chambers like miniature storage vats. Indians, as well as others in these regions, eagerly search out these nests to secure the swollen ants. Biting off the abdomen yields a sweet mouthful as though one were eating delicious sweet grapes.

SOME FAMILIAR ANTS

The genus *Formica* contains many familiar species of ants. Although much smaller than the species of *Camponotus*, many of them are more formidable.

The Sanguinary Ant, *Formica sanguinea*, also called the red ant, or red slave maker, constructs no mound but loves an old stump or log. It is only three-eighths of an inch long or less, but does not hesitate to raid a colony of ants of much larger individuals and much greater numbers. Although it will attack the nests of a number of species, its favourite victim is *Formica fusca*, whose pupae it loves to steal. These are carried home by the raiders, and carefully reared so that eventually they can take over a large share of the work in the nest.

The Negro Ant, *Formica fusca*, has a great many subspecies and varieties, and is widely distributed throughout Europe and North America. It is a timid ant and constructs small nests.

The Common Red Ant, *Formica rufa*, also called hill ant, or horse ant, is also widely distributed in Europe and North America. It is easily recognized by the rather large mounds which it constructs. Under tall trees in open woods are favourite locations. The pupae are gathered in large quantities, particularly in Europe, and when dried are sold in pet shops as the familiar "ant eggs" for bird and pet food.

The Allegheny Mound-building Ant, *Formica exsectoides*, is another species that builds large nests. These may be four or five feet in diameter and two feet high. A single colony may occupy several mounds in the vicinity. The mated queens cannot initiate a colony but get their start in a queenless or declining colony of *Formica fusca subsericea. Exsectoides* ranges from Southern New England and New Jersey westward into Ohio. It is most abundant in the Allegheny Mountains of Pennsylvania.

THE DARK BROWN ANTS AND THE CORNFIELD ANT

Lasius niger and *Lasius flavus* are common species in Europe, where they are called dark-brown ants. *Lasius niger* is represented in North America by the subspecies *Lasius niger americanus*, the Cornfield Ant.

The cornfield ant is well known for its care of colonies of root aphids. In the autumn, the aphids are carefully placed along the roots of various grasses reached by means of tunnels. Here they remain throughout the winter and early spring. As soon as corn is planted and sufficiently started, the ants transfer the aphids to the corn plants.

All summer the aphids are tended for their secretions, or honeydew, which the ants collect at frequent intervals.

THE DRIVER ANTS—MARCHERS OF THE TROPICS

The genera *Eciton*, of the American tropics, and *Dorylus*, of the African tropics, comprise the driver ants, which appear in adventure stories as the ferocious ants ready to pursue and attack us if we don't watch out! These tales are far from true, although it is a fact that the driver ants are voracious and prey upon insects. They will attack birds, mammals, or humans only if for some reason these creatures are injured and unable to get away.

The driver ants build no nests, and, when not on the march, cluster in what is called a bivouac. When on the march, they extend out through the jungle in long lines, while individuals forage on all sides. On balance, their foraging habits are probably more beneficial than harmful to man, because they clean up the area through which they march.

The Indians and other natives living in their palm-thatch huts look forward to the appearance of driver ants. These people simply go outside and let the insects swarm through their homes, knowing that, when the ants have passed, every other insect, cockroach, fly, and spider will also be gone. Their only worry is that the colony might suddenly decide to bivouac for the night or longer in one of the houses, a situation not very pleasant for the occupants.

CUTTERS OF LEAVES

The Leaf-cutting, Parasol, or **Fungus-growing Ants** are interesting tropical species. They build underground nests, which in a prosperous colony may be of considerable size. The author has seen nests on the tributaries of the upper Amazon that honeycombed the ground for a diameter of thirty feet and to a depth of eight or nine feet.

The workers of this group travel out from the nest, along trails measuring three or four hundred feet, to species of trees which have leaves suitable for their use. Pieces of leaf of a size convenient for them to carry are cut out and carried back to the nest. This they do by holding the piece of leaf in their jaws, the edge resting in a groove on the top of the head. As they travel the trail homeward, each carries a piece of leaf which looks like a little parasol, which is why we call them parasol ants. To one seeing this for the first time, it is a strange and fascinating sight.

A PATH IN THE JUNGLE

So numerous are the individuals engaged at this leaf-cutting work that large trees can be stripped of their foliage in a single night. Often, when such numbers of ants follow the same trail, a path six or seven inches wide and several inches deep is worn in the jungle floor.

The leaves are carried home, not for the ants to feed upon, but to make beds in which the spores of a certain kind of fungus will be planted and grown by the ants. It is this fungus upon which the ants feed.

ANTS THAT CAN SEW

Some species of the tropical genus *Oecophylla* can sew! They stitch leaves together to make their large nests in forest trees. For needles and thread they use silk-spinning larvae. Holding the larvae in their jaws, the ants work the larvae back and forth to pull the edges of the leaves together and to fasten them with the silk.

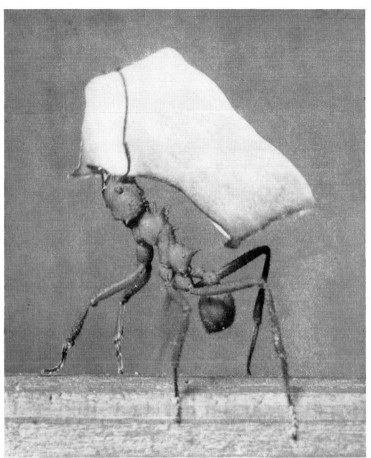

A LEAF-CUTTING OR PARASOL ANT

This ant is carrying part of a green leaf to its nest underground, where the leaf will be used in a bed to grow fungi for food. Parasol ants live in huge colonies sometimes thirty feet across and eight to nine feet deep. The nest is mostly below the surface of the ground; only a small mound at the top shows its location. *See page 1998.*

AN ANT EMERGING FROM ITS PUPAL CASE

Nurse ants will clean up this young one, and may feed it its first few meals. Soon it will start work; first it will serve as a nurse ant, but later it will graduate to a field ant job. Notice that the ant's eyes are not so large as those of some other insects—living in burrows and close to the ground, it has little need for keen vision. Ant pupal cases are sold as "ant eggs", a bird food. *See page 1992.*

A WORKER WASP GOES ABOUT ITS HOUSEWORK

This wasp appears to be busily examining a larva, to see how it is developing; later, when it emerges as an adult, it too will take over some of the duties of the wasp colony. All around the worker you can see empty cells, some still with ragged edges. These the worker will clean up, so that the queen may lay more eggs in them. Unlike bees, wasps feed mainly on insects.
See page 2001.

SOLITARY WASPS

The solitary wasps (superfamily Sphecoidea), as their name indicates, live by themselves rather than in a colony. They dig a burrow in the ground, or construct cells of clay, or tunnel out a pithy stem. In these burrows they store living spiders or almost any kind of caterpillar which they have paralysed by stinging. On their victims, they lay their eggs, thus ensuring that their larvae will be well supplied with fresh food.

The Giant Cicada-Killer, *Sphecius speciosus* is the largest wasp in this group. It has to be large in order to capture a cicada and carry it to the burrow it has dug in advance.

THE GIANT CICADA-KILLER SUBDUING A VICTIM

A large and beautiful wasp, the giant cicada-killer has a black body with yellow marks on it and its wings are shining amber. After digging a burrow, the female catches a cicada, paralyses it with her poison sting, and deposits it in the burrow. Her egg is laid on the still living victim, so that the young wasp larva may have fresh food when it hatches.

A beautiful insect dressed in shining black, this wasp is patterned with yellow marks, and borne on flashing amber wings. It is not so beautiful to the impatient householder, however, when one, or more, of these wasps selects his recently established lawn as a suitable medium in which to make its three-quarter-inch-round burrows. The large size and the colouring of these wasps attract attention, and they are frequently brought into the author's office by people who have never seen them before.

There are a number of very pretty wasps in the genus *Sphex*. Many of them are marked with red, and their waists are long and very slender. They use caterpillars for the most part to stock their burrows.

Chlorion ichneumonea is a large wasp, beautifully coloured, with a reddish abdomen, golden hair on its thorax, and amber wings. It is

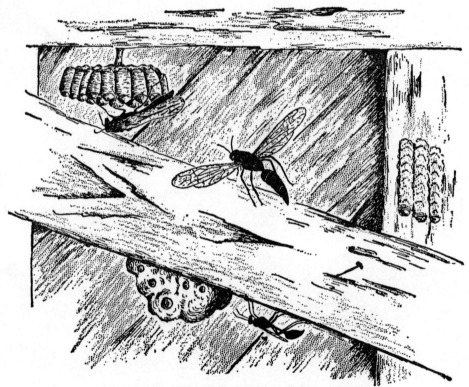

**SOME WASPS BUILD APARTMENT DWELLINGS,
OTHERS LIKE TO LIVE ALONE**

In the upper part of the picture, Polistes wasps are building a paper-walled multiple dwelling, suspended from a rafter by a stem. (They chew wood pulp to make their strong paper.) As the apartment becomes larger, they will add more stems. Down below, a slender mud dauber builds its house of clay. Away over to the right are the rows of cells built by another kind of mud dauber.

frequently seen in the autumn in America about the flowers of boneset and joe-pye weed.

Chalybion caeruleum, an iridescent, steel-blue wasp, is one of our familiar mud daubers that are continually building their clay nests under the eaves of our houses, and in attics whenever the windows are left open. In the nests of *caeruleum*, the cells are piled one on top of the other.

Sceliphron cementarius is another of our familiar mud daubers. It is a blackish wasp; the basal parts of the legs are yellowish. This wasp carefully arranges its cells in rows of about five to eight cells. The rows are laid side by side, making a flat mud nest. This and the preceding species collect spiders to stock their nests.

TYPICAL WASPS, HORNETS, AND THEIR RELATIVES

The superfamily Vespoidea is a division of the Hymenoptera with which most people have some acquaintance. Its members—wasps, hornets, and their kind—are usually called the social Hymenoptera, because most of them live in colonies or large families. A few of them are solitary, and none of them are genuinely socially inclined, especially if they feel that their personal activities are about to be interfered with. They defend their rights in a vigorous way with their powerful stingers.

Left to their own devices, they will attend strictly to their own business.

VELVET ANTS—THEY ARE REALLY WASPS

The so-called "velvet ants" are not ants at all, but brightly coloured wasps. If you don't believe this, just try picking one up. You will drop it in a hurry.

The females are wingless and densely covered with hair. Frequently a bright-red colour, banded with black or white, and with a velvety sheen, they are attractive insects as you see them hurrying over a sandy spot or other dry or desert location. Some in the American Southwest have white or yellow hair which may be long and shaggy. The males are winged, and although brightly coloured are quite differently marked from their mates. They sport about, visiting the flowers on sunny days. You can pick up a male without fear, for he cannot sting.

The velvet ants belong to the family Mutillidae, numbering over three thousand species. They vary in size from a tiny one, *Mutilla lilliputiana*, which is about an eighth of an inch long, to the giant of the family, *Dasymutilla occidentalis*, an inch or more in length. This large species, occurring in the south-eastern United States, is called the Cow-killer Ant.

Although the Cow-killer is certainly a wicked stinger, its ability to kill a cow is doubtful.

Velvet ants are invaders of the nests of bees, where they feed upon the larvae of the rightful owners. On the whole, the family is a delightful one to study as well as to collect.

POTTER WASPS—THEY BUILD WITH CLAY

The sculptors of the wasp world, these wasps belong to the family Eumenidae. It is a large family, but few people are at all familiar with any of the species. Although all use clay in some way for the construction of their nests, only a few of these wasps can be said to be true artisans.

The best of the potters is the eastern North American species, *Eumenes fraterna*, which builds a perfect clay jug. About half an inch in diameter, spherical in shape, with a contracting neck and a flaring top, the little jug perches on the upper side of a twig or leaf.

The wasp does not leave the jug open, for any possible intruders, but fits a perfectly modelled clay lid on it. Several paralysed, but still living, cankerworms are stored within the jug. Suspended by a silken thread over the supply of food is the wasp egg, soon to hatch and feed upon the worms, but held safely out of harm's way in case a worm should suddenly lash its body about.

The Heath Potter, *Eumenes coarctatus*, builds its nest of three or four cells joined side by side on a twig. A great many of the family make use of hollow twigs or tubes, simply placing clay walls across the hollow, making a continuous row of cells. The family is widely distributed throughout the world; the heath potter is a native of Europe.

TARANTULA HAWKS AND THEIR RELATIVES

Long-legged, slender, solitary wasps, black or dark blue in colour, and frequently ringed with a bright-orange or red band, might belong to the family Psammocharidae, in some books called the Pompilidae.

Psammochares atrox is a common species in the eastern United States. India claims the honour of having the smallest and the largest members of this genus yet known. They are *Psammochares mirandus*, less than a quarter of an inch long, and *ilus*, about one inch in length.

POTTER WASPS ARE SKILLED ARTISANS

The potter wasp builds a perfect little jug of clay about one-half inch in diameter on the branch of some convenient tree, fills the jug with paralysed cankerworms, and suspends an egg within easy reach of the living food. Then it fits a lid over the mouth of the jug, to protect the egg. Potter wasps are valuable—they help keep down the pests that attack fruit trees, slaying great numbers of injurious insects each year.

All of the other species of the family are dwarfed by some of the genus *Pepsis*. These are the Tarantula Hawks. Some of them reach a length of two inches, with a wingspread of nearly four inches. *Pepsis obliguerugosa*, an all-blue insect, is the largest. A close runner-up is

Pepsis formosa, blue with red wings. Both occur in the South-west of the United States, where the tarantula, their normal prey, is plentiful. The spiders are paralysed by stinging, then stored in an underground burrow, where the wasp larvae feed upon them. The only species in the East, *elegans*, is much smaller. It is generally blue, with orange wings.

PAPER-MAKING WASPS

The family Vespidae is well known, for it includes most of the social wasps.

It contains three genera which may be easily distinguished by the types of nests that they build. They are, *Dolichovespula:* nest above ground, suspended from trees or shrubs; *Vespa:* nest above ground, but in hollow trees, stumps, old buildings, or caves; and *Vespula:* nest underground, occasionally in the base of stumps.

The White-faced Hornet, *Dolichovespula maculata*, is the most familiar member of the first group. It is the big, burly, black wasp, with white body markings and a conspicuous whitish face, that builds its paper nest in fruit trees or lilac bushes. The well-known paper-making wasp, it uses the wood fibre from old weathered fences, buildings, or dead trees to construct its nest. The nest is started in the spring by a single queen and reaches its full size, usually larger than a football, by autumn. The entire colony, except for a number of young mated queens which will hibernate in old logs or other shelter, dies at the first severe frost.

Somewhat similar species in Europe are *silvestris* and *media; arenaria* is not common in North America; while *norwegica* occurs in both Europe and North America.

The Giant Hornet, *Vespa crabro*, is as large as, if not larger than, the white-faced hornet. It is European, but was introduced into the United States sometime before 1854, for it was in that year that it was first discovered. The wasp has made itself quite at home and is now reported from New England to Maryland; it has even crossed the Appalachians into Ohio. The queens are frequently seen in the spring, investigating old stumps and logs for possible cavities in which to start a colony.

There are half a dozen species of the genus *Vespula* in the United

States. They are the familiar yellow jackets, and all of the species look pretty much alike.

Although smaller than the other social wasps, these creatures make up what they lack in size by the viciousness of their sting and their seeming desire to use it. On the slightest disturbance of the everyday

THE BALD-FACED HORNET MAY JOIN A PICNIC

Big black fellows with white faces, the bald-faced or white-faced hornets like to build their large paper nests in fruit trees or taller shrubs. The young queen starts her colony in the spring, and her offspring work at their nest (*shown in background*) until autumn frosts come. Now all die except next year's queens, which retire to sleep in some old stump until the following spring. Like all wasps, the white-faced hornet loves to sip fruit juices or other sweet liquids, and may join a picnic party.

activities of the nest, the workers surge forth to do battle or die in the attempt. These black-and-yellow, uninvited guests at picnic gatherings make themselves obnoxious as they dispute the right to sandwiches and jam, even crawling into our mouths to steal a bite.

Their nest is enclosed in paper and always placed underground, in a mouse's burrow, perhaps, or even in a slight hollow under a tuft of grass. The author has, on a few occasions, found a nest in a hollow stump and even between the walls of an old building (particularly where considerable debris had filtered down between the walls), and in the sawdust-filled walls of an icehouse. The common North American species are *Vespula pennsylvanica*, *maculifrons*, and *squamosa*. The European species is *vulgaris*.

POLISTES WASPS

One other important family of social wasps is Polistidae, with several common species living in the United States. They are largish wasps, about one inch long, reddish black or brown, with smoky wings. The combs or nests, without any enclosing envelope of paper, are hung by a short central stem, or, if very large, by several stems, in a corner of a building, under the eaves, around windows, or may even be placed in the corner of a door frame.

As is the case with most of the social wasps, the overwintering young queen starts the colony by building a few cells of the comb. In each cell, an egg is laid. The little grubs hatching from the eggs are fed by the queen until they pupate. When the young wasps develop, they are the workers or imperfect females and take over the work of the colony.

The two common species of this family in the eastern United States are *Polistes annularis* and *pallipes; texanus* and *aurifer* are two of the common western species.

THE BEES

THE BUMBLEBEES

Familiar insects to all of us are the bumblebees, also called humble-bees or carder bees.

Most people, however, think of them as the big, burly, yellow-and-black bees that visit our flower gardens, dragging the blossoms groundward with the weight of their bodies.

Although many bumblebees are as large as an inch or more, there are some species less than three-eighths of an inch long. In a single colony, there is also a great variation in the size of the individuals, for besides the queen, which is the largest, there are the workers, which are small to medium in size, and the males, which fall between the workers and the queen in size.

As with the wasps, the colony is started by the young queen, who has spent the winter season in a log under debris, under brush, or in a sheltered corner. She starts her nest in a hollow in the ground or under a tuft of grass. Here she makes up a number of balls of pollen and nectar in which the eggs are laid. The bees from these eggs are workers that now take over the nest duties. Brood cells are built, and nectar and pollen are gathered to feed the hungry little larvae. From this modest beginning in spring, a nest occupying a hole ten to twelve inches wide may develop by autumn.

The nests are nicely constructed. The hole in the ground is lined with bits of dry plants or straw. In the centre of this, the nest proper is located.

Unlike most of the social wasps, the bumblebees do not construct an envelope around their brood cells.

Bumblebees, having tongues much longer than those of honeybees, are very useful for pollinizing blossoms with long corollas. The clovers and alfalfa are among these, and without bumblebees it would be impossible for these plants to seed. Flower growers who specialize in long-tubed flowers like the columbine hate the bumblebees. These flowers are too long-tubed for even the bumblebees to reach, so the rascals go around behind and cut a slit in the flower's nectary, stealing the nectar without pollinizing the flower, instead of letting a long-tongued moth do the good deed.

THE HONEYBEES

The honeybee is undoubtedly one of man's most important insects. Having been associated with him for over four thousand years, it is frequently regarded almost as one of his domesticated animals. Only recently, however, has man been able, through breeding, to change to any great extent the character of the bee.

It is true that man has long put the bee to good use, and the bee has responded by adapting very readily to all the artificial devices invented, such as modern hives, section boxes, and innumerable other things to make beekeeping simpler and easier. But, left to themselves, bees will as readily desert all of these for a hollow tree and unconcernedly continue the same life they have followed for centuries.

The honeybees belong to the family Apidae, and the familiar species is *Apis mellifera*. (This name seems to have three years' priority over the name *Apis mellifica*, which was generally used a few years ago.)

There are a number of other species of *Apis*, but none of them have been much use for beekeeping. There are, however, many races of the honeybee. Four of these are of outstanding importance.

BEES—TOP-RANK ASSISTANTS TO FARMERS

While earthworms pulverize the soil, making it possible for plants to grow, bees pollinize the flowers, enabling plants to fruit. All of the thousands of species of bees perform this service. The honeybee (*top*) also provides mankind with honey. Seventeenth-century colonists took domestic bees to America from Europe, and the many wild honeybees now found in the United States are descendants of early imports. The gorgeous bumblebee (*bottom*) has a long tongue and pollinizes many of the tubular flowers, especially clover.

Four Important Honeybees. The German honeybee, which had its origin in central Europe, is blackish, very unfriendly, and little used now in the United States. The Italian honeybee, which originated in Italy, ranges from dark to golden in colour, is gentle in temperament, and is now the most widely used in the United States. The Caucasian honeybee, which originated in the Caucasus, is greyish, the gentlest in temperament. The Carniolan honeybee, which originated in Austria, is grey with white bands, gentle, and very little used in the United States.

Castes Among the Honeybees. Like the bumblebees, the honeybees have three castes in each colony. The queen is a female and is the mother of the colony. She is developed from a fertilized egg through being fed on special food called "royal jelly". The workers, of which there are a great number, frequently amounting to fifty thousand in an active colony, are abortive, or neuter, females, developed from fertilized eggs, but fed on "bee bread", a mixture of pollen and honey. The drones are sexual males, developed from unfertilized eggs; they have no stings.

Unlike the bumblebee colony, the honeybee colony lives over the winter and may go on year after year, unless some interruption or trouble occurs. During the winter, a cluster of bees is maintained, the temperature in the centre being kept sufficiently high so that brood rearing is carried on in a very limited way almost throughout the winter. The outer bees of this cluster act as insulators, and are constantly changing places with those nearer the centre, thus seldom becoming chilled.

How the Honeybees Swarm. During the height of the summer season queen cells are built. Just before any of the queens are ready to emerge from their cells, the old queen leaves with a large collection of workers of various ages and functions, also some drones, to found a colony in a new location. This is called swarming. The first young queen to come out of her cell, if the colony is still quite populous, may leave with another swarm. This is called after-swarming. Some of these after-swarms may be so weak, having only a few handfuls of workers, as to be unable to establish a colony.

When the colony is reduced to a low point where no more swarming can be indulged in, the young queen then in the colony will be allowed to tear down the remaining queen cells and sting the occupants to death. Her sting is used only on a rival queen. You yourself can handle her, and she will never once make any attempt to sting. The workers will kill a queen by "balling" (surrounding her in a living mass of bees; but will never use their very efficient stingers on her.

They will use their stingers in every possible way to protect their colony.

The Oriental Hive Bee, *Apis indica*, is the largest of the honeybees. It reaches a length of nearly three-quarters of an inch, and builds a single comb three to six feet long. This is fastened to the limb of a tree, a ledge of rock, or an old building. This bee occurs throughout India, Ceylon, and Malaysia. Distributed through the same area is the smallest bee, *Apis florae*, measuring three-eighths of an inch or less.

STINGLESS BEES

To most people, stings and bees are always associated, but there are some bees that are stingless. Although they cannot sting, to many people they are just as bothersome as the stingers. Ordinarily, they will not bother anyone, but disturb their nest and they are out in numbers. They get into your eyes, ears, and nose; they crawl under your clothing, they crawl into your hair, digging with their legs, and biting with their mandibles. They love to nibble at tender places on your skin.

There are about three hundred species of stingless bees ranging throughout the tropical and warmer parts of the world. In the Americas, they extend from central Mexico to southern Brazil and northern Argentina. Like their close relatives, the honeybees, they are social insects, gather nectar and pollen, and build combs; their combs, however, are in horizontal layers, instead of vertical.

These creatures usually construct their nests in hollow trees, on rock ledges, old walls, or even among rocks on the ground, and in matted vines. The entrance is almost always a tube, frequently a number of inches in length.

The stingless bees (family Meliponidae) are much smaller than the honeybees. The largest is less than three-eighths of an inch, and the smallest is a tiny creature, a trifle more than one-twelfth of an inch. In some countries, the honey stored by these bees is gathered for use. Before the introduction of the European or German honeybee into the Americas, the Indians used this honey, and even went so far as to establish colonies of the bees in artificial hives. Attempts are being made to revive and commercialize stingless bees as honey producers.

Explorers or others should be careful in using such honey, for that made by some species is highly poisonous. Stingless bees are not at all averse to gathering secretions from other sources than the nectar of flowers. The author has frequently seen these insects collected by the dozens around the bodies of dead animals as well as other refuse.

OTHER BEES

There are many other species of bees, belonging to a number of families. (All make up a superfamily, Apoidea.) Many of these have extremely interesting habits. The Xylocopidae, the burly Carpenter Bees, look like big black bumblebees. The Megachilidae, the dainty Leaf-cutter Bees, usually green in colour, make cells of pieces of leaves in the stems of pithy plants or other small openings.

The rest of the bees, belonging to many families, are mostly solitary in habit. Each has its own life history, sometimes a rather complex one. You will find it fascinating to study any one of them that you happen to notice.

Index to Black-and-White Plates

Where a single page number is given in this Index, the illustration faces that page. Where two page numbers are given, separated by a hyphen, the illustration will be found between the two pages indicated.

Index

[161-1]   American eagle. See page 969

[161-1A]   American elk. See page 726

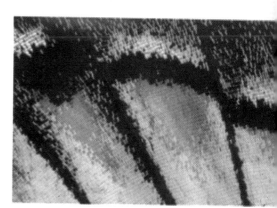

[161-1B]   Binturong. See page 542

[161-1C]   Bobcat. See page 565

[161-1E]   Butterfly wing scales. See page 1900

[161-1D]   Blue heron. See page 926

[161-1F]   California rattlesnake. See page 1379

[161-2]   Scaup *(rear)*, Canvasback. *See page 949*

[161-2C]   Water Moccasin. *See page 1376*

[161-2D]   Cottontails. *See page 244*

[161-2A]   Caracara. *See page 958*

[161-2E]   Elephant trunk. *See page 630*

[161-2B]   Cecropia moth head
                See page 1928

[161-2F]   Goshawk. *See page 960*

Caprimulgus, *europeaus*, 1061
vociferus, 1061
Caprolagus, 236
Capromys pilorides, 370
Capuchin, 166-167
white-throated, 167
Capybara, 294, 361-363
Carabao, 768-771
Carabidae, 1841, 1846
Carabus, 1847
Caracal, 567-568
Caracal caracal, 567
Caracara, 958-959
Audubon, 958-959
Caracul, 845
Carangidae, 1541, 1544
Carassius auratus, 1464
Caraya, 164-166
Carcajou, 515-518
Carcharias taurus, 1408
Carcharodon carcharias, 1409
Cardinal, 1163
Cardinal fish, 1530
Caretta caretta, 1278
Cariacu, 736-737
Cariama, 1005-1006
grey, 1005
Cariamidae, 1005
Caribe, 1470-1472
Caribou, 711, 743-751
Barren Ground, 743, 747-749
Greenland, 749
mountain, 743
Old World, 743, 749
woodland, 743, 748, 749
Carnegiella strigata, 1472
Carnivores, 425, 426 ff.
Carp, 1455, 1462-1464
leather, 1463
mirror, 1463
scaled, wild, 1463
Carpodectes nitidus, 1107
Carteria lacca, 1805
Cascabela, 1368
Cashew bird, 982
Casmerodius albus, 928
Cassidinae, 1893
Cassidix mexicanus, 1152
Cassowary, 886, 891, 892-893
two-wattled, 892
Castor canadensis, 299
fiber, 299
Castoridae, 300
Casuariidae, 892
Casuarius casuarius, 892
Cat, 559-599
African wild, 561, 563
Andean highland, 572
bashful, 153-155

Cat, bay, 571
black (marten), 513-514
black-footed, 563
Chinese money, 571
civet, 529, 539-544
desert, 571
Egyptian fettered, 563
European wild, 562
fishing, 570
flat-headed, 570
Geoffroy's spotted, 572
golden, 571
grey wild, 563
hydrophobia (skunk), 529
jungle, 563
Kaffir, 561, 563
Manx, 561
marbled, 570-571
marsupial, 42-43
miner's (cacomistle), 482-484
otter, 572
Pallas, 571
pampas, 572
ring-tailed, 482-484
rusty spotted, 571
Scotch wild, 562
sebala, 563
Siamese, 561
swamp, 563
wild, 559, 561-567
See Cheetah, Civet cat, Cougar, Jaguar, Leopard, Lion, Lynx, Ocelot, Panther, Tiger, Wildcat
Catamblyrhynchidae, 1160
Catamblyrhynchus diadema, 1160
Catamount, 573-576
Cataphracti, 1605
Catbird, 1129
Caterpillar, 1645, 1752, 1923-1952, 1987
European tent, 1943
forest tent, 1943
geometer, 1944-1945
great basin tent, 1943
hedgehog, 1935
saddleback, 1947
salt-marsh, 1935
sea, 1681
silkworm, 1927-1928, 1943-1944
slug, 1946-1947
tent, 1941-1943
tussock, 1939-1941
woolly bear, 1935
See also Butterfly, Moth
Caterpillar hunter, 1946-1848
fiery, 1847-1848

Caterpillar, green, 1846-1847
Catfish, 1455, 1456, 1475-1481, 1527
electric, 1478-1479
sea, 1475-1477
Cathartes aura, 972
Cathartidae, 972
Catlocarpio siamensis, 1459
Catostomidae, 1455
Catostomus commersonni, 1456
Cattle, 765-786
humped, 771-772
shorthorn, 766
Texas longhorn, 766
wild, 772
Cattle warble, 1974
Caudata, 1195
Causus rhombeatus, 1365
Cave-swiftlet, 1067
Cavefish, North American, 1485
Cavy, 359-361
greater Patagonian, 360-361
mara, 360-361
Patagonian, 360-361
Cayuse, 653
Cebi, 167
Cebidae, 160
Cebus, 166
Cecidomyiidae, 1961
Celithemis, 1788
elisa, 1788
eponina, 1788
ornata, 1788
Cenozoic era, 864, 866-868
Centipede, 1747-1748
Centrarchidae, 1533
Centriscidae, 1516
Centrocercus urophasianus, 996
Centropomidae, 1529
Centropomis undecimalis, 1529
Centropristes striatus, 1537
Centropus phasianinus, 1053
Cephalopod, 871
Cephalopoda, 1692, 1707
Cephalopterus ornatus, 1107
Cephalorhynchus, 409
Cerambycidae, 1843, 1885
Ceratacanthus schoepfi, 1624
Ceratomegilla fuscilabris, 1860
Ceratotherium simum, 675

[161-3]   Gnus. See *page 809*

[161-3A]   Guinea pig. See *page 359*

[161-3B]   Hippopotamus. See *page 692*

[161-3C]   Horse and colts. See *page 651*

[161-3D]   Lizard. See *page 1282*

[161-3E]   Macaws. See *page 1044*

[161-3F]   Mourning dove. See *page 1037*

[161-4]   Pelican and cormorant.
See pages 913-18

[161-4D]   Quail. *See page 983*

[161-4A]   Penguin. *See page 897*

[161-4E]   Raccoons. *See page 480*

[161-4B]   Dog-face butterfly. *See page 1921*

[161-4F]   Ringed plover. *See page 1015*

[161-4C]   Porcupine. *See page 354*

I

Ibex, 840-842
  Abyssinian, 841
  Chetan, 841-842
  Nubian, 841
  Pyrenean, 842
  Siberian, 841
Ibis, 933-935
  glossy, 934-935
  sacred, 934
  scarlet, 934
  white, 934
  white-faced glossy, 934
  wood, 933
Ice Age, 872, 873
Ice bird, 910
Ichneumia, 548
Ichneumon, 547-548
Ichneumon fly, 1928
  1931, 1989-1992
Ichneumon (mongoose),
  547-548
Ichneumonoidea, 1990
Ichthyomys, 315, 316
Ichthyosaur, 869, 1239
Ichthyostege, 870
Ictailurus planicept, 570
Icteridae, 1149
Icterus galbula, 1153
  parisorum, 1153
Ictinia mississippiensis,
  960
Ictonyx, 514
Idothea metallica, 1727
Iguana, 1283, 1289-
  1300, 1303
  desert, 1291
  Galápagos land, 1292-
  1293
  marine, 1284, 1292-
  1293
  tropical, 1283, 1292
Iguana iguana, 1283,
  1290
Iguanidae, 1289
Imantodes gracillimus,
  1377
Impala, 821-823
Inca, collared, 1075
Indicator indicator, 1099
  xanthonotus, 1100
Indicatoridae, 1100
Indri, 148-150
Indridae, 150
Insecta, 1714, 1749
Insectivora, 65
Insects, 1643-2011
Invertebrates, 1643-2011
Io moth, 1932-1933
Irbis, 579-580
Irediparra gallinacea, 1030

Irena, 1127
Irenidae, 1127
Iridoprocne bicolor, 1125
Isia isabella, 1936
Isindi, 267
Isoptera, 1743, 1773, 1994
Isospondyli, 1433
Istiophoridae, 1596
Istiophorus americanus,
  1594
Isurus glaucus, 1409
  oxyrinchus, 1409
Ithaginis cruentus, 985
Ixobrychus exilis, 931

J

Jacamar, 1090-1091
  bronzy-breasted, 1091
  great, 1091
  paradise, 1091
Jacamerops aurea, 1091
Jaçana, 1012, 1029-1031
  American, 1031
  comb-crested, 1030
  pheasant-tailed, 1031
Jacana spinosa, 1031
Jacanidae, 1030
Jack, 1527, 1541
Jack rabbit, 236, 238-
  241
  Allen's, 240-241
  black-tailed, 240-241
  California, 240-241
  Espiritu Santo Island,
  241
  grey-sided, 240-241
  white-sided, 239-240
  white-tailed, 238-239
Jackal, 439-442
  black-backed, 441
  grey, 441
  Himalayan, 441
  side-striped, 442
  silver, 450
  yellow 441
Jackass 658-660
Jackass laughing, 1082
Jackass bat, 122
Jack-smelt, 1519
Jacksnipe, 1014
Jaculus, 349
Jaeger, pomarine, 1012
Jaguar, 574, 592-595
Jaguarius onca, 592
Java man, 141
Javeline, 691-692
Jay, 1178-1179
  blue, 1178-1179
  California, 1179
  Florida, 1179
  scrub, 1179
  Steller's, 1178

Jellyfish, 1661, 1666-1668,
  1671-1672
  comb, 1661, 1671-1672
  common, 1667
  common comb, 1671
  flat, 1666
  Florida, 1676
  many-tentacled, 1666
  moon, 1667
Jentinkia, 484
Jerboa, 330, 341, 348-350
  African three-toed, 349
  Australian, 341
  big-eared, 350
  dwarf, 349
  fat-tailed, 349
  flat-tailed, 349
  jumping, 330, 341, 348-
  350
Jerboa marsupial mouse,
  43
Jerboa rat, jumping, 330,
  341, 348-350
Jersey cow, 766
Jewfish, spotted, 1537
Jigger, 1745-1746, 1985
  United States, 1745-1746
Johnny darter, 1528-
  1529
Joint snake (lizard),
  1286
Jointworm, 1689
Jumbo, 633-634
Jumping bean, Mexican,
  1952
Jungle fowl, red, 990
Jungle sheep (deer), 715
Junonia coenia, 1910
Jurassic period, 869, 878
Jutia, 369, 370
Jynx torquilla, 1097

K

Kagu, 1004-1005
Kaibab, 262
Kangaroo, 59-64
  blue flyer, 62-63
  dusky tree, 64
  forester, 60-62
  great, 60-62
  great grey, 62
  musk, 64
  rat, 60
  red, 62-63
  tree, 63-64
Kangaroo mouse, 345-347
Kangaroo rat, 292-294,
  341
  American, 341
  banner-tailed, 294
  dwarf, 294
Kapoune, 49

[161-5]   Rhinoceros. *See page 670*

[161-5A]   Ring-billed gull. *See page 1024*

[161-5B]   Scarlet ibis. *See page 934*

[161-5C]   Scarlet king snake. *See page 1344*

[161-5E]   Sparrows. *See page 1164*

[161-5D]   Skimmer. *See page 1028*

[161-5F]   Tern. *See page 1027*

[161-6] Toad. See page 1218

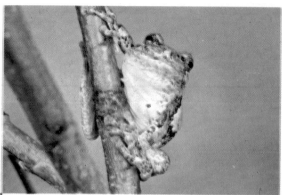

[161-6A] Tree frog. See page 1237

[161-6B] Virginia rail. See page 1008

[161-6D] Vulturine guinea fowl. See page 994

[161-6C] Vulture.
          See page 970

[161-6E] White heron. See page 928

[161-6F] White-tail fawn.
          See page 733

Index to Colour Plates

Where a single page number is given in this Index, the illustration faces that page. Where two page numbers are given, separated by a hyphen, the illustration will be found between the two pages indicated.

IN ADDITION TO FREELANCE PHOTOGRAPHERS GUILD
AND NATIONAL AUDUBON SOCIETY,
CREDIT FOR COLOUR PHOTOGRAPHS IS GIVEN AS FOLLOWS:

Cy Alexander 13-1A; 14-8B; 16-2A, 8;
161-2C, 161-5D
E. Anderson 1-C
Art Publishers, Ltd. 8-10A
D. W. Barber 9-2A; 161-1D
Jack Breed 11-5
E. Butterfield 6-1A
Camera Hawaii 13-2A
Lynwood M. Chace—UPI 15-2B, 3A, 4B, 5,
5A, 6, 7; 16-2, 3A, 5, 5A
Gordon Chambers 16-6
Chicago Natural History Museum 5-7;
6-6A; 7-6A, 12
Melvin Cohn 1-12
H. Harold Davis 8-14A; 10-1A
Walter Dawn 4-1; 8-3A, 3B; 9-4, 4A, 13,
13A; 10-3, 5A, 8, 10; 11-7A, 7B, 9A, 9B,
14; 14-7A, 7B; 16-7
Jack Dermid 1-1, 5; 3-4, 13B, 14A; 6-13;
8-7A, 9C, 10; 9-1B, 9A, 11C, 16; 10-1, 5,
5B, 5C, 8A, 11C, 12, 14, 14B; 11-8, 13,
13A, 15A; 14-10B; 15-1A; 161-5C, 6F
H. Dinsch 8-6A
Louis Doff 4-16A; 5-3A, 4, 13; 7-10A, 12A,
13B; 8-7C
Ray Endicott 3-8A
R. S. Eshmeyer 1-H; 12-2B, 6, 6A, 7, 7A, 8,
8A, 9, 9A, 14, 14A, 16, 16A; 14-7
S. C. Feiker 8-5B; 9-2; 10-2; 12-1; 14-15A
John S. Flannery 8-13, 13A
Commander Atillio Gatti 1-E, 2, 2A; 2-1,
4, 7; 3-15A; 4-9; 5-7A, 8, 10, 11, 11A;
6-1, 2, 4; 7-2, 5; 8-2, 13B, 16A; 11-7;
161-3B, 4A, 6D
H. L. Gibson 15-6A; 16-3
Ormond Gigli 14-13A
Nelson B. Gilbert 7-11

Robert E. Gossington 11-14B
Graphic House 1-9, 9A; 7-5A; 9-7A; 10-15
Arthur Griffin 8-3
E. P. Haddon 11-8B, 10B, 11A
Dick Hanley 1-7
William J. Jahoda 3-6; 9-11; 10-2A, 2B, 7B,
9A, 9B, 11, 11A, 11B, 14A; 11-1A, 3A,
3B, 4, 16; 12-3B, 3C, 4, 4A, 4B, 5, 10, 12,
12A; 14-5B, 8, 8A, 11A, 14, 14A, 16;
15-2, 4, 4A, 7A, 14; 16-1, 4A, 6A; 161-1E,
2B, 6A
B. E. Johnson 3-2A, 3-6A, 13A; 4-8; 5-12A;
6-2A; 8-8A, 9; 9-10; 10-12A, 15C; 12-3,
3A, 15, 15A; 13-1; 161-1, 2, 2A, 2D, 4D
H. W. Johnson 8-16
Bert Kempers 14-10A, 11; 161-1A, 6
Weldon King 7-8A, 9, 9A; 8-11
Wallace Kirkland 3-9; 5-5; 8-2A; 9-8; 10-9,
16
Herbert C. Lanks 1-N, 1, 4; 3-3A, 14; 4-7,
14; 6-10; 8-14; 10-16A; 11-9; 15-3, 15
John M. Linder 15-8, 8A, 8B, 8C
Tom McHugh 1-K, P; 5-1
Mac's Foto Service 1-F, G; 3-12A; 5-5A,
8A, 14, 15; 6-16A; 8-11A; 9-4B; 12-5
Lewis S. Maxwell 11-8A; 14-16A; 15-1, 2A,
14A; 16-1A
Meston's Travels, Inc. 2-12, 14, 14A, 15,
15A; 4-2A; 6-3; 7-7, 7A, 10; 8-5C, 12;
9-7, 7B; 11-6, 10, 11, 13B; 13-13; 161-3E
Sam Oppee 2-16
Charles J. Ott 5-1A; 161-4C
Edwin C. Park 3-1, 1A, 7, 7A, 10A, 10B,
12; 4-6, 6A; 5-9; 6-14, 14A, 15, 15A; 7-6,
13A; 8-4, 8-5A, 8, 9B, 15; 9-5, 11A, 14A;
10-4; 11-16A; 161-1C, 4E
Clifford G. Pepper 1-M

Understanding
the Weather

PEOPLE are always talking about the weather, and with good reason. The weather has a vital bearing on our plans, our work, our leisure, and even on our dispositions. Weather is important in great and small things—all the way from planning a picnic to growing successful crops and keeping our nation and the world well fed.

Children are even more dependent than grown-ups on the state of the weather. Clear sunshiny days mean happy play out-of-doors; rain often means the opposite, to many a mother's despair; an abundance of snow promises endless hours of merriment on a strange and wondrously transformed landscape. So, be it fair or foul, weather is always a meaningful and absorbing topic to explore with children. They are keenly interested in it even before they can talk, and words like "rain" and "sun" are often among the first they learn.

Later on, as the children grow older, flashes of lightning, claps of thunder, blizzards, wind, rain and ice storms give rise to a never-ending series of *whys* and *hows*. They discover a fascinating fellow called the weatherman; the younger ones may be under the impression that he "makes" the weather, but the older ones sagely pooh-pooh this juvenile belief and ask to know something of the secrets of weather forecasting.

In our grandparents' time people relied on various signs for hints of coming weather. Some of these signs we still believe in—on the whole, with good reason, as they often have scientific backing. Others are wholly unreliable and have no such backing; where they "work", the effect is wholly coincidental and cannot serve as a basis for further prediction.

RING AROUND THE MOON

Perhaps you have heard that "a ring around the moon means rain". This old belief is accurate enough—rain often follows the appearance of a moon halo. The big question—and it is sure to come—is *why*. The ring indicates that the moonlight is refracted (bent) by ice particles in clouds that are miles overhead. Those ice particles warn us of a change of temperature, and thus of a probable change in weather.

THE RAINBOW HAS PRACTICAL VALUE

"Rainbow at night, sailors' delight; rainbow in the morning, sailors take warning", is another fairly accurate saying. Rainbows are formed when raindrops in the air break up the sunlight into distinct colours. This takes place in the part of the sky opposite the sun. When you see a rainbow in the late afternoon sky, you know that the moisture causing it is to the east. Why? Because the rainbow must be opposite the sun, which is now in the west.

Now add to this the pertinent bit of information that our storms usually move from west to east; you can see that the moisture (a potential storm), being already in the east, has passed us. But, by the same reasoning, a morning rainbow (in the west while the sun is in the east) means that there is a large amount of moisture in the west. It also means that as this comes toward us, it is likely to arrive as a storm.

NIGHT RAINS

"Rain before seven, shine before eleven", is likely to prove a dependable forecast if the rain is light or moderate. Rain usually lasts only a few hours; and when it starts in the cooler hours of the night, the morning sun often evaporates the clouds and stops the rain. However, the proverb does not apply to heavy storms that are often connected with north-east or southerly winds.

WHEN THE SUN "DRAWS WATER"

Still another weather prediction we can depend on to a certain extent is that rain is on the way if we see "the sun drawing water". This expression, which is used to describe light rays streaming toward the setting sun, is inaccurate.

Actually the rays are formed by sunlight streaming through openings in the clouds and shining on vapour. However, as the rays appear when there is an exceptional amount of moisture in the air and when the sun is hidden behind a cloud, it often happens that they come before rainy weather. But often, of course, they do not.

UNRELIABLE PREDICTIONS

Among the many false notions is the one that we can tell how many days will pass before it rains by counting the number of bright stars within a ring that may be around the moon. Another entirely incorrect idea is that whenever the moon goes into a new phase, the weather changes.

If all these old tales were true, the weatherman could close up shop. As it is, he has to stay on the job twenty-four hours a day, using the most modern equipment devised by scientists; and at that he cannot be as certain as he would like to be! But more of this later.

The Wind and Its Ways

We can blame most of our severe storms on the wind. Rain is not unpleasant unless it is lashed by strong winds. Snow usually seems very beautiful—unless wind turns it into a blizzard. Windstorms, unaccompanied by rain or snow, often do fearful damage, especially in the form of tornadoes and hurricanes.

The air that is all about us is made up of a number of gases— chiefly oxygen and nitrogen. Although we cannot see these gases, they have mass, and gravitation pulls them downward, giving them weight. As a rule you do not think of the pressure of air against your body; but when you drive from mountain heights to a lower level the change to "heavier air" is very noticeable—especially on your eardrums.

HOW WINDS ARE FORMED

For a number of reasons we have high-pressure areas, in which the air is cooler and therefore more compact, and low-pressure areas, in which the air is warm and expanded. (One reason for this is that different portions of the surface of the earth heat up or cool off at unequal rates.)

Wind is air moving from high-pressure areas to areas of low pressure. The winds are due to nature's effort to equalize pressure differences in the atmosphere.

A high or low-pressure area may range from a few hundred to a thousand miles in diameter. In a "high", the pressure increases steadily toward its centre, and in a "low" it gradually decreases. The speed of a wind depends on the degree of pressure difference between a low-pressure area and the high-pressure area next to it. When we have stormy weather these variations show up sharply on the weather map in your daily newspaper; this is an especially good time to study the weather map with your child.

Why It Rains

"Look at the *size* of those raindrops!" is an exclamation that may start a child wondering about why we have raindrops at all, and why they are of varying sizes.

The "makings" of rain are around us all the time—tiny droplets of water that we know as vapour and bits of water-attracting dust. These dust particles—two important kinds are salt from the sea, and smoke—become the centre of the droplets when the vapour in the air takes the form of moisture. Air can hold only a certain amount of vapour (warm air can hold more than cold air), and when there is too much vapour, the droplets of water join together and form raindrops.

How Air Currents Affect Rain. When the raindrops are formed in gently rising air, the condensation takes place very slowly and quite small drops may fall in a drizzle. But when the drops are formed in powerful upward currents, the drops may be held aloft until they are very large (to a fifth of an inch in diameter). This kind may fall with great splashes—the kind you often see just before a thunderstorm downpour. At times the larger raindrops flatten out and split up as they fall.

Sun Showers. Occasionally we have the odd effect of rain falling from a clear sky overhead. This may be due to the drops being delayed in their fall by rising air currents or by friction with the air. Thus before the drops reach us the clouds from which they started have blown away or evaporated.

Another curious sight is rain falling on one side of a street while the other remains dry. This is simply caused by small clouds meeting with a cold air current that turns their vapour into raindrops which fall only over the area the clouds had covered.

A child may think of rain as blowing to his neighbourhood from great distances—possibly from over the ocean. This is never the case: rain falls where it forms. The moisture may have been absorbed into the air many miles away, but it is never blown to us as "ready-made" rain.

Billions of Snowflakes, No Two Alike

Probably no other event in nature is so thrilling to children in our latitudes as the first snowfall of the season. It is as if snow were a substance designed to turn the humdrum world into a dazzling fairyland. Observation only strengthens the fairyland illusion, for if a youngster studies a flake through a magnifying lens, he notes that each snow crystal has a lovely, delicate design, as if woven on a fairy loom.

Though billions of snowflakes may fall, no two are exactly alike in design, except that *each one* is six-sided. Some flakes, as you can see with a magnifying glass, are more solid than others. They are formed in clouds very high above the earth. The most beautiful flakes are of lacelike design, and they usually form in warmer air currents, close to the earth.

SNOW AND SLEET

"Aren't snowflakes frozen water?" your alert child may wonder. "What makes them soft and white? Why aren't they little pieces of ice—like sleet?"

Good questions, these. Snowflakes *are* frozen moisture, like ice, but they are formed when the moisture in the air condenses (changes from vapour to liquid form) at a point below freezing. If, on the other hand, the moisture condenses into rain first and *then* freezes, sleet results. The time when the freezing takes place accounts for the difference.

SNOW IS MOSTLY AIR

As the crystal particles of the snowflake take shape, many tiny reflecting surfaces are formed with air spaces between them. It is these air spaces that make snow soft and dazzling white as it reflects the light of sun and moon. Also, it is odd but true that the fluffy, new-fallen snow forms an effective blanket, protecting whatever it covers from freezing. (Air is one of the best insulators against heat and cold.) Newly fallen snow usually contains only one part of ice to ten or twelve parts of air; and even snow that has been lying for some time is at least half air.

The popular theory that the temperature may be "too cold for snow" is definitely wrong. The extreme dryness of very cold air does make heavy snow unlikely, but even then a warm wind may move into the upper atmosphere bringing moisture with it and thus resulting in snowfall.

Frost on the Windowpane

The appearance of frost on windowpanes is nature's artistic announcement of the arrival of winter. In some homes, where storm windows are used, this lovely effect is not so common; but sooner or later most children have an opportunity to see these exquisite icy window decorations. It is pleasant to credit them to the magical hand of Jack Frost, but they are of course the result of low temperatures outside, cold enough to chill the indoor air which touches the windowpane. (Storm windows protect the pane and prevent frost from forming on windows.)

If the chill is sufficient to cause the moisture to condense on the inner surface, frost begins to form. Usually crystals first appear around some tiny irregularity in the glass surface or around a grain of dirt. Often these first crystals continue to grow, and as some of the smaller ones evaporate, their moisture condenses again on the larger crystals. Thus spectacular designs, numerous and interestingly varied, are created.

HOW TO MAKE FROST PRINTS

As window frost rarely lingers more than a brief time, children may get a great deal of pleasure from making prints of some of its lovely designs. This may be done with blueprint paper. Sheets of this paper, about twelve inches square, should be kept in a dark place until ready for use. Some morning when the sun is shining brightly though frost prints have not yet melted from the window, take a piece of blueprint paper and quickly attach it with scotch tape to the pane. Press the sensitive side directly against the frost design for two or more minutes.

The sunlight turns parts of the paper light blue but leaves the pattern of the frost in white. Remove the sheet of paper and immediately immerse it in a pan of clear water for a few minutes. Then transfer it to another pan of water to which a tablespoon of peroxide has been added. When the blue part has turned an attractive shade, rinse the paper in clear water, then spread it flat to dry. It will make an attractive decoration for any child's room.

Hail—"Hot-Weather Ice"

To some people, hail is "hot-weather ice", as it is usually seen during violent summer thunderstorms; it is quite rare in wintertime. Hailstones are formed when raindrops are caught in swiftly uprushing air and are carried high into the cloud tops where they may meet snow crystals. Mixing with the crystals, the raindrops become globules of cloudy ice. These globules may fall, on descending air currents, into warmer rain levels of air and take on a layer of ice from contact with rising drops. Again the growing ice pellets may be tossed far up, and again a layer of snowy ice will be added to them.

This up-and-down movement may continue until the ice pellets have a dozen or more layers. Records show that hailstones having twenty-five layers, and as big as baseballs, once fell at Annapolis, Maryland!

Thunder and Lightning

Many children are frightened by thunder and lightning. Their timidity usually fades in the course of time if they see that grown-ups are undisturbed by storms, and if they can understand just what takes place during a storm. This last, unfortunately, is easier said than done.

It is easy for a child to believe that there is such a thing as air all about him, for he can often feel it blow. It is more difficult for him to understand that electricity is always there as well. Nevertheless, every bit of dust and droplet of moisture has its charge—a fact closely connected with lightning flashes. It may be enough to explain to a young child that lightning is electricity—the same force that furnishes our modern lighting—but on a grand scale. Older children may be eager for more details.

WHAT CAUSES LIGHTNING

About the time a thunderstorm breaks, you may notice a wind spring up as though from nowhere and blow toward the storm. Scientists believe such currents of air may be part of a chain of events somewhat of this order: as the wind blasts its way upward, it cools and the vapour in it is changed to liquid form. The speed of the rising current tears apart the drops of water that form. The fine drops are carried to the top of the storm cloud while the larger drops fall to lower levels.

Now, it seems that the fine drops have a negative charge, while the large drops are positively charged. When the electrical pressure between these two parts of the cloud becomes powerful enough to break through the air so that they can join each other, a tremendous spark—lightning—is created.

"LIGHTING" IN A STORAGE BATTERY

If you are interested in things electrical, and have some simple equipment, you probably know how to give your child a dramatic illustration of how lightning is formed—and thunder too. All you need do is connect the positive and negative poles of a storage battery with a piece of wire. As the youngster looks on, he will see how quickly a spark is created there, caused by the negative particles (electrons) leaping toward the positive pole. He will hear, too, a crackling sound accompanying the spark.

In just the same way the giant sparks that flash across the sky produce a crackling sound of tremendous volume. We call it thunder.

FORKED LIGHTNING AND OTHER KINDS

Lightning comes in different forms. The most common type is forked lightning with a brilliant zig-zag flash, as the electrical discharge takes the path of least resistance—an irregular one—through the air. A second kind, "sheet" lightning, is caused by a flash hidden in the clouds which brightly but briefly lights up a whole cloud or a sheet of rain.

Finally, there is "heat" lightning—a description we often give to a sudden lighting of the atmosphere that appears near the horizon though no thunderclouds are in sight. Heat lightning is usually explained as the reflection of lightning flashes below the horizon by the hazy air within our range of vision. It is appropriately named "heat lightning", as we encounter it during hot, muggy weather.

WHEN LIGHTNING IS DANGEROUS

Though we want to reassure a child on the subject of lightning, we must not fail to let him know the circumstances under which it can be a real danger. Most flashes are from one cloud to another; very few come down to earth, and only when the negative charges in a cloud are attracted to positive charges on the ground.

Probably the safest place to be is indoors when there is a storm in your neighbourhood. If you happen to be outdoors and without available shelter, be sure to avoid high ground, trees standing alone, the edges of woods, and wire fences. In case the lightning is unusually severe and directly overhead, your safest course is to lie or sit in a ditch.

HOW MANY MILES BETWEEN YOU AND LIGHTNING?

Most children enjoy being able to reckon how far lightning is from them; and knowing how to do this is especially comforting to the nervous child who imagines that every flash is directly over his head. The calculation is based on the lapse of time between a flash and the moment the resulting thunder is heard. So quickly does light travel that the lightning is seen almost the instant it flashes. Therefore, if you count the number of seconds that elapse between the flash and the thunder, you know, roughly, the distance between you and the storm centre.

You can train yourself to count seconds without a timepiece by repeating some such phrase as "storm in the sky", which takes a second to say. A lapse of fifty seconds means the lightning is about ten miles away (a mile distant for each five seconds). You cannot hear thunder from a greater distance than ten miles, except under unusually favourable circumstances.

THUNDERSTORMS

You have probably noticed that there are different kinds of thunderstorms and that they have different effects on the atmosphere. Moreover—contrary to popular belief—they may even occur in winter. The two kinds that most often visit us in summer are the local or "heat" thunderstorms and the "cold front" type.

Heat Thunderstorms. The heat thunderstorm is generally a small-scale affair leaving the atmosphere as oppressive as before it broke. This kind is most common in the late afternoon or early evening following an extremely hot day. The overheating of the surface air when the atmosphere is fairly quiet brings about an unstable condition, and the storm is the outcome.

"Cold Front" Thunderstorms. The "cold front" type of thunderstorm is frequently more severe. It may form a nearly continuous line hundreds of miles long where cool air from the west or north meets hot, moist currents. As a result, the vapour in the air turns rapidly into water, and with the heavy downpour of rain great electrical disturbances take place. Such a storm is often accompanied by wind squalls and hail. Though it may break at any time of day or night, the most likely time is in the afternoon.

Winter Thunderstorms. Winter thunderstorms, which usually come at night, almost always announce the arrival of a sharp change in the weather. Towards the close of a cold spell, when a warm wind blows over a region, thunderstorms may occur whenever there is a great contrast between the cold and warm air masses. Or again, where warm air currents are being displaced by cold air, thunderstorms may give warning of the coming cold wave.

Storms of Violence

TORNADOES—SEVERAL HUNDRED MILES AN HOUR

The thunderstorm is a relative of the dreaded tornado and often accompanies it. The tornado has a distinctive feature: it always includes a funnel-shaped whirling cloud. This terrifying spiral, green grey to yellowish black, moves at a rate of thirty to fifty miles an hour, and within the tornado itself the wind moves at more than a hundred miles an hour!

In fact, the speed of a tornado has been estimated up to several hundred miles an hour; but since recording instruments are destroyed in such a storm, no exact records are available. Fortunately, tornadoes do not occur everywhere, and even in regions where they are apt to strike they are infrequent.

CYCLONES—A CONFUSING TERM

Many people use the term "cyclone" for these violent storms. In fact, the "cyclone cellar" is the common description of an underground retreat used for escaping tornadoes. The word is rather confusing, for to weathermen a cyclone is a low-pressure area which is not violent and may extend over thousands of square miles. These cyclones pass over us every few days and generally cause no more of a change than increased cloudiness.

However, it became customary to apply the term "cyclone" to a certain type of storm that developed about low-pressure centres in the Indian Ocean. From this the usage of the term broadened until it became identified with tornadoes.

Hurricanes—Several Hundred Miles Wide. A hurricane is not accompanied by a funnel-shaped cloud; but its speed may reach 150 miles an hour and the width of its path is far greater than that of a tornado. This width is generally several hundred miles. Hurricanes always start on the ocean.

Forecasting the Weather from the Clouds

CLOUDS AND FOG

The best way for a youngster to "get the feel" of a cloud is simply to walk through fog—for fog is nothing more than a cloud in contact with the ground or a body of water. Once a child knows that cloud and fog are the same, his logical question then is, "What keeps some clouds up in the sky?" and, "Why don't they fall down to earth like this one?"

FEATHERY AND BILLOWY CLOUDS

These questions are fairly easy to answer if we can forget that constantly repeated phrase, *"floating* clouds". Clouds really do not float; they tend to fall earthward. However, certain forces act to prevent their falling. For example, the great billowy white mounds that we call cumulus clouds are supported by the strength of ascending air currents. In the more feathery (cirrus) type of cloud formation we may see some of its moisture fall as snow or rain; yet the cloud stays aloft if conditions favour condensation, and if the particles it has lost are replaced.

Most clouds are formed by rising, warm, moist air that becomes visible as billowy masses of moisture when it comes in contact with the cold upper atmosphere; and generally this same process which produces clouds helps to counteract their natural tendency to fall earthward.

We get fog when warm, humid air meets a cool surface such as that of a lake or sea, or ground which has rapidly lost the heat it absorbed during the day. As in the case of clouds, the vapour in the warm air then condenses and becomes visible.

HOW TO READ THE CLOUDS

Anyone, young or old, enjoys playing the role of weather prophet. While many factors enter into the predictions made by the weatherman, you can nevertheless have the fun of making reasonably accurate forecasts just from clouds. And because you are concerned only with your immediate vicinity, your prediction may be more successful than that of the professional forecaster!

As far as a youngster is concerned, the simplest indications for clear weather are high, white clouds, while dark, heavy, low clouds point to bad weather. Long before people knew much about clouds, this much was about all that anyone looked for in them. Today, however, we have the benefit of years of study of the clouds, and we know that scientists have divided them into three general classes. Each class has its own story to tell about conditions high above the earth.

SPECTACULAR CUMULUS CLOUDS

The spectacular cumulus is the kind of cloud that children are likely to notice first. Its name, taken from the Latin word for "heap", is a good description; these clouds are heaps upon heaps of billowy mounds that may reach a height of several miles! The name becomes easy to remember when you associate it with "accumulated".

When cumulus clouds are glistening white they are an indication of good weather; but on a summer afternoon they may gradually darken and become an unmistakable threat of a storm—often accompanied by thunder and lightning.

Artists are fond of ornamenting their landscapes with cumulus clouds, but the cloud "portraits" they produce are often decidedly incorrect. They show the clouds as rounded masses at both top and bottom—whereas the base of a cumulus cloud is always flattened.

The base forms at the level where rising warm air cools enough to cause its water vapour to condense. Then, if the current of rising air is strong, the cloud grows upward with its rounded head marking the top of the rising air column.

CIRRUS CLOUDS—"MARES' TAILS"

The white feathery wisps that you are likely to see on a fine summer day belong to a second cloud group. These are cirrus clouds (from the Latin word meaning "curl"). "Cirrus" sounds a little like "icy", and this helps us remember that cirrus clouds are made up of tiny particles of ice—not merely moisture. They are the highest of all clouds, and may range from two to seven miles aloft. As cirrus clouds suggest long wisps of hair, they are often called "mares' tails".

If cirrus clouds are moving from the south-west, the temperature is apt to fall. If they are coming from the north, it is probably going to be fair and warm.

STRATUS CLOUDS

Thin flat clouds make up the third group, well named "stratus", for this is the Latin word for "spreading out". Stratus clouds do spread out across the sky, sometimes as far as we can see. To remember this name, think of the similarity of "stratus" and "straight". Most often the stratus clouds appear as low, grey sheets. They may merge with rain clouds and precede a storm, or they may clear away like lifting fog.

OTHER CLOUD FORMS

"Nimbus" is one of the descriptive words that are frequently combined with the three cloud forms when dark, heavy portions build up in them. For example, a cumulus that grows black and threatening is a cumulus-nimbus, and a nimbo-stratus is a rain sheet.

"Alto" ("high") is also combined with cloud names, and "fracto" ("broken") is another element of cloud descriptions. Add these terms to combinations of main cloud forms like cirro-cumulus and cirro-stratus and you have a descriptive name for all the many cloud formations that decorate the sky. Cirro-cumulus clouds are small and fleecy, and are arranged in even rows high overhead, thus producing what we often call a "mackerel sky"—a sign of coming rain.

How the Weatherman Operates

Young children sometimes look upon "the weatherman" as a very definite person—either a hero or a villain, depending on how well the weather fits in with their plans. Of course it does not take long before they realize that this somewhat mysterious figure has nothing to do with producing rain, snow, or sunshine—he only predicts them. In the next stage they begin to wonder why, when predictions prove wrong for several days, we show any further interest in them.

FORECASTING THE WEATHER

We can understand why some predictions fail to materialize when we have a clear picture of the complex factors that enter into weather forecasting. A large country's Weather Bureau has perhaps hundreds of observers stationed throughout the entire country. In a typical organization each observer reports by teletype to his headquarters all the weather facts in his region as recorded on sensitive instruments. These facts are all immediately recorded on a map by symbols.

The Chief Forecaster studies this map, compares it with the weather map of the previous day, and prepares his predictions. Similar forecasts are made for other sections of the country and a radio station in the Weather Bureau broadcasts them, while teletype sends them to airports, newspapers, and commercial organizations. A daily weather map is also printed and widely distributed.

Yet, despite all the skill and care of the experts in reading signs, it is not always possible to be certain about the coming weather. An unexpected shift of winds may blow storm clouds from an area that was prepared for rain, and drench another where sunshine was expected!

The Weatherman's Tools. The observers who report to the Weather Bureau depend on a variety of instruments. The weather vane, which indicates wind direction, is the one with which most children are familiar. More complicated are the barograph which writes down the pressure of the air, the anemometer which measures the speed of wind, thermometers, a very precise barometer, an instrument to measure moisture, and another to record sunshine. These tools, and many others, help the observers to prepare their account of weather conditions close to earth.

Studying the Upper Atmosphere. Besides assembling this information, weathermen have become increasingly interested in ascertaining the condition of the upper atmosphere. To obtain this data the Weather Bureau sends aloft equipment attached to a large balloon. A radio device called a radiosonde is attached to a parachute carried in the balloon. This instrument is a small radio station in effect, telling, as it rises, about the temperature and winds, as well as other conditions.

The information supplied by the radiosonde is recorded on a complicated receiver at the Weather Bureau. The parachute carries a small balloon which both prevents the larger one from going up too fast and also helps to steady it. When they reach fifteen hundred feet, the smaller balloon bursts, causing the remaining balloon to rise faster—which it does for about thirteen miles. Then the larger balloon bursts—the parachute opens—and the radiosonde descends safely.